ON MORAL C

C000138601

Lessons from
Research Ethics

What can we learn from the past that may be relevant to modern clinical research ethics?

In this book Allan Gaw and Michael Burns show us how the past can illuminate the present and help us understand where we are and how we have come to be here. The authors present a series of intriguing stories that take us from a ship in the Royal Navy in the mid 18th century to a backwater in the US in the early 19th century and on to Cuba at the dawn of the 20th century, by way of the offices of a Harvard academic and a courtroom in Nuremberg. On this journey through the history of research ethics we are shown examples of the best and the worst. In each case the theme is one that is relevant today and one, which, if we are involved in clinical research in any capacity, we must address.

Allan Gaw, MD, PhD, FRCPath, FFPM is Director of Operations at the Glasgow Clinical Research Facility. He is the author or editor of 16 books including the companion volume *Trial by Fire: Lessons from the History of Clinical Trials.* You can learn more about him and his work at www.allangaw.com

Michael H.J. Burns, BSc is a Research Fellow at the Glasgow Clinical Research Facility.

SELECTED OTHER WORKS

Gaw A. *Our Speaker Today – A Guide to Effective Lecturing.* SA Press, Glasgow, 2010.

Gaw A. *Trial by Fire – Lessons from the History of Clinical Trials.* SA Press, Glasgow, 2009.

Gaw A, Murphy MA, Cowan RA, O'Reilly D St J, Stewart MJ and Shepherd J. *Clinical Biochemistry An Illustrated Colour Text.* 4th edition, Elsevier, Edinburgh, 2008.

Lindsay GM and Gaw A. (Eds) *Coronary Heart Disease Prevention: A Handbook for the Health-care Team.* 2nd edition, Harcourt Brace, Edinburgh, 2004.

ON MORAL GROUNDS

Lessons from the History of Research Ethics

Allan Gaw

Michael H. J. Burns

First published 2011
by SA Press
4 Birkdale Wood, Westerwood, Glasgow, G68 0GY

Printed in the United Kingdom by Clydeside Press

British Library Cataloguing in Publication Data
A catalogue record for this book is available from the British Library.

ISBN 978-0-9563242-2-1

For those who taught us right from wrong

In actual fact it is absolutely impossible for experience to establish with complete certainty a single case in which the maxim of an action in other respects right has rested solely on moral grounds and on the thought of one's duty. It is indeed at times the case that after the keenest self-examination we find nothing that without the moral motive of duty could have been strong enough to move us to this or that good action and to so great a sacrifice; but we cannot infer from this with certainty that it is not some secret impulse of self-love which has actually, under the mere show of the Idea of duty, been the cause genuinely determining our will. We are pleased to flatter ourselves with the false claim to a nobler motive, but in fact we can never, even by the most strenuous self-examination, get to the bottom of our secret impulsions; for when moral value is in question, we are concerned, not with the actions which we see, but with their inner principles, which we cannot see.

· ■ · ·

The practical imperative will therefore be as follows: *Act in such a way that you always treat humanity, whether in your own person or in the person of any other, never simply as a means, but always at the same time as an end.* We will consider whether this can be carried out in practice.

Immanuel Kant, *Groundwork of the Metaphysic of Morals*
Translated by HJ Paton

CONTENTS

FOREWORD

The 18th century Prussian philosopher Immanuel Kant noted, "we cannot do morality a worse service than by seeking to derive it from examples." And, went on to say: "Imitation has no place in morality, and examples serve us only for encouragement..."

Encouragement is, however, no bad thing. By being shown that what any moral law commands is in fact possible and practicable, we may be convinced that morality is indeed possible in practice. By studying examples of the best and the worst, we can examine the specifics of any general and necessarily abstract universal moral law. Those specifics will be different for every field, and in the case of clinical research they will turn on issues such as respect for the individual, the concept of consent and the prevention of harm. Although Kant seems to eschew the merit of studying such practical examples, in fairness he only does so if we are trying to use them to derive a universal law of morality. Quite correctly, he argues that it is only if we have such a moral law in the first place that we can judge the morality of any given example.

Where then should we look for our encouragement in the form of examples? For those who work in clinical research, perhaps they need do nothing more than raise their eyes and look around them. However, for those who are not already active research professionals, or for those who seek more engaging narratives, we may plough the rich furrows of the past. Our subject has a long history and the question of what is morally permissible within the context of clinical research has been asked for centuries. During that time the moral frameworks on which we hang our decisions have changed and developed.

This is not a book of moral philosophy, but we have felt the need to lay some foundations upon which we can build the historical narratives and their contemporary significance. These foundations are laid in the introductory chapter, where we present a brief discussion of the moral principles that are currently in use. Inevitably we have had to discuss Kant and his work as he is at the centre of much of what has been written on the subject. Kant, however, has a tendency to frighten people. Even as German philosophers go he is regarded as a challenge and one of his eminent translators has described the title of his book on ethics as nothing less than "horrifying".

To balance Kant's approach we also look at other possible moral frameworks comparing them and contrasting them as necessary. From there we will follow five different themes, using a key historical narrative to illustrate it and to prompt the discussion of its contemporary relevance. Each story – whether it be from the 18th-20th centuries – informs us and stimulates a discussion of 21st century ethical issues. In each case we can enjoy the narrative from the safe distance that history affords us, but we should also use the examples to help us question our current practices. Sometimes the past sheds light on our current problems; at other times it casts shadows. In either case we can learn from the past, and this book is written on the premise that our most beneficial, and our sternest, tutor can be history itself.

· ▪ ◼ ▪ ·

ACKNOWLEDGEMENTS

The idea for this book came out of discussions with colleagues and students who have attended our various lectures and courses on the History of Clinical Research. In particular, we must acknowledge the debts we owe to those who have kindly read and commented on early drafts of the chapters. These are Shona McDermott, Liz Tolmie, Anne Gordon and Judith Godden. Despite their valuable input we emphasise, however, that any factual errors or pieces of clumsy prose that remain are entirely our own.

We must also thank other individuals and organizations for various acts of kindness that helped with researching of the topics, the sourcing of illustrations or the production of the book.

David Tolmie – for help with the cover design.

Liz Ronald – for help in taking the manuscript to the finished book.

Maria Burns – for help with editing of the authors' photographs.

United States Holocaust Memorial Museum – for allowing us to use the image of Leo Alexander.

Iain Milne from the Royal College of Physicians of Edinburgh Library– for allowing us to use the image of the James Lind plaque.

Joan E. Klein & Sonya Coleman from the Claude Moore Health Sciences Library, University of Virginia – for allowing us to use images from the Walter Reed archive.

Ngaire and Hilary Watson from New Zealand – for allowing us to use Dr Malcolm Watson's photograph of Maurice H. Pappworth.

Clare Harrison & Valerie McClure at the Library of the Royal College of Physicians and Surgeons of Glasgow who helped us with access to the original works of James Lind and William Beaumont.

World Medical Association - for allowing us to reproduce the Declaration of Helsinki.

Andrew Smith, Editor of the journal *CRFocus* – for allowing us to re-publish versions of Chapters 2, 3 and 4 that were previously published as articles in *CRFocus*.

While every effort has been made to identify the copyright holders of the photographs used in the book, several have remained elusive. If you hold the copyright of any unattributed image, please contact us and we will ensure this is corrected in any subsequent edition of the book.

Finally, we would like to thank our editor at SA Press, Moira Mungall, without whose encouragement and patience there would have been no need for any acknowledgements, for there would have been no book.

· ■ · ·

I

"Never simply as a means"

The search for a moral framework

Clinical research presents us with a moral dilemma. In order to discover new medical knowledge that will be applicable to all, we must first subject some individuals to interventions that may be harmful. These interventions might, in other circumstances, be considered inappropriate or even, in some cases, criminal. We justify our actions by seeking the consent of study participants, and we make efforts to ensure that this consent is informed and freely given. Overall, we have a duty to respect the autonomy of individuals. Indeed, when a study protocol is evaluated from an ethical perspective, it is this feature that will figure prominently in the decision. But, words like *autonomy* and *consent* and *respect* and *duty* are terms that have varied and diverse meanings, and which are open to different interpretations.

In order to deal with the moral dilemma at the heart of clinical research, perhaps we need to start at a more basic level of understanding, and build from there. In other words, to discover what makes something right in the context of a clinical experiment, we must first ponder the deeper question of what makes anything *ever* right or wrong. When we have examined how we make ethical decisions in our daily lives, then we may be able to consider the morality of clinical research in a new, brighter light.

Before we go on, a word about nomenclature: in this book we will use the terms 'ethics' and 'morality' interchangeably. Some philosophers draw a distinction between them, but many do not. Indeed, both terms have their roots in words for 'customs', the former being a derivative of the Greek, and the latter of the Latin. (1) In the context of clinical research, however, we more commonly talk of ethics, especially of the ethical approval given by Research Ethics Committees.

THE CENTRAL QUESTION

When we think of the ethics of clinical research, or indeed of any field, the central question raised is: how do we decide if an action is morally permissible? No matter where we stand on the moral spectrum there will be some things we find acceptable, and others we will not. In some areas there may also be a remarkable consensus on what is right and what is wrong. For example, it may be generally agreed that it is unacceptable to lie to a patient in order to induce her to participate in a clinical trial. But, why do we think it is not morally permissible to lie in such circumstances, or even in any other context? How do we come to this conclusion? Broadly, three answers to this question may be offered:

1. I should not lie, because to do so would breach a basic moral principle.
2. I should not lie, because to do so would have unfavourable consequences.
3. I should not lie, because to do so would not be virtuous.

Three schools of philosophical thought are encapsulated in these three answers. The first of these approaches is that of the *deontologist*, the second, that of the *consequentialist* and the third, that of the *virtue theorist*. Let us look at these three approaches in turn.

DEONTOLOGY

In Greek the word *deon* means a duty or obligation. Thus, deontology is an ethical framework that judges the morality of an action based on the adherence of that action to a duty or set of duties. These duties are usually laid out in the form of rules or principles. (2)

There are many contenders for such rules – some of which lay claim to their authority from their divine provenance, in that they are believed to have been given to mankind by God. Indeed, one of the most ubiquitous moral rules that figures in all of the major world religions has come to be known as *the Golden Rule*. (3) In the Christian tradition, this is usually given in the form from the Gospel of St Luke: "Do unto others as you would have them do unto you." (4) In Confucianism, we find: "Is there any single saying that one can act upon all day and every day? The Master said, Perhaps the saying about consideration: 'Never do to others what you would not like them to do to you.'" (5); in Hinduism, from the Mahabharata: "One should never do that to another which one regards as injurious to one's own self. This, in brief, is the rule of Righteousness."(6); in Islam, from the Farewell Sermon of Muhammad: "Hurt no one so that no one may hurt you."(7); in Buddhism, from the Dhammapada: "He who seeking his own happiness punishes or kills beings who also long for happiness, will not find happiness after death." (8); and finally in Judaism: "You shall not take vengeance or bear a grudge against your kinsfolk. Love your neighbor as yourself: I am the LORD." (9)

Such an ethic of reciprocity is therefore widely preached, and has formed the foundation stone of many moral systems. However, specifically in the context of medicine, we have another contender for the universal rule or over-riding moral principle: the Hippocratic Oath. This oath includes the pledge "to abstain from whatever is deleterious and mischievous." (10)

Over time a simplified, ethical slogan has evolved from this to encapsulate the Hippocratic tradition: *Primum non nocere* or *First, do no harm*. The origins of this exact phrase are obscure, but can be traced back, not to antiquity, but to an attribution to the 17th century English physician known as the English Hippocrates, Thomas Sydenham, in a 19th century work. (11)

The chief contender for a universal rule, however, may be that reasoned by the 18th century Prussian philosopher, Immanuel Kant (fig. 1). His contributions to this field are undoubtedly the most important of the last 500 years and any contemporary discussion of moral philosophy, whether it agrees with his stance or not, cannot ignore it. His slim, but seminal volume, *Groundwork of the Metaphysic of Morals*, takes as its main topic the search for a supreme principle of morality. (12)

As noted in our foreword, Kant was disdainful of merely observing good and bad actions in order to derive from such examples a moral law, for he argued that the only way we can decide if something is good or bad in the first place is by applying some pre-existing rule.

Figure 1. Immanuel Kant (1724-1804). Steel engraving by J. L. Raab, 1791 after a painting by Döbler.

Thus, through reflection and by reasoning from first principles he generated what he referred to as the Categorical Imperative, from which all other moral laws may be derived. He stated this Categorical Imperative in a number of forms – the most famous of which is:

> *Act only on that maxim through which you can at the same time will that it should become a universal law.* (12)

A practical moral imperative that is derived from this, or which some would argue is merely a rephrasing of it, runs as follows:

> *Act in such a way that you always treat humanity, whether in your own person or in the person of any other, never simply as a means, but always and at the same time as an end.* (12)

It is this form that is most routinely discussed when we think about the ethics of clinical research, for it is immediately apparent that we may as investigators use study participants "simply as a means" to our ends rather than apportioning them the respect they deserve as "ends in themselves", i.e. as rational individuals with personal autonomy.

Kant's moral philosophy is, however, too much for some. They would like a moral framework based on principles that they can apply in practice, but not one that acts as a moral straightjacket. Kant, for instance, argued that to lie was wrong no matter what the context. Most of us living in the real world could readily offer examples of times when it is not only permissible to tell a lie, but, because of the circumstances, virtually mandatory. If we choose to be deontologists, how then can we be less constrained, allowing context to have some influence on our moral decisions?

Figure 2. W.D. (Sir David) Ross (1877-1971).

Sir David Ross (fig. 2), a Scottish philosopher, put forward in his book *The Right and the Good* in 1930, just such an alternative. (13) He argued that what makes an action right is not the motive from which it is done, nor its consequences, but whether it accords with one or more of a set of self-evident *prima facie* duties. He listed seven such duties:

- Fidelity: the duty to act in accordance with explicit and implicit promises, including the implicit promise to tell the truth.
- Reparation: the duty to recompense someone you have previously wronged.
- Gratitude: the duty to benefit people who have done you service.
- Justice: the duty to ensure people get what they deserve.
- Beneficence: the duty to help other people in respect of their virtue, intelligence or pleasure.
- Self-improvement: the duty to improve ourselves with respect to virtue or intelligence.
- Non-maleficence: the duty to avoid harming others.

It is notable that two of these duties - beneficence and justice – are, along with respect for persons, at the centre of the moral framework for the conduct of clinical research as set out in the Belmont Report from 1974. This is a highly influential document that has shaped US policy on the conduct of clinical trials (14), and which we will discuss further in chapter 4.

Interestingly, considering our original question of whether we may lie to study participants, honesty is not one of the self-evident duties put forward by Ross. He argued that to lie was morally wrong only when it went against another duty, such as a promise to tell the truth. This approach obviously allows context to play a role and allows some flexibility in our application of the rules. Some argue that Ross's account of morality is much less demanding than that of Kant, but that it is this very modesty which gives it its strength as a theory. (2)

Objections

One of the major criticisms of deontology is an apparent paradox at its core. (2, 15) Central to the notion of deontology is that there are things that we must do, and others that we must not. In other words, there are constraints on our actions.

This paradox turns on the fact that constraints are placed on us in order to prevent us doing something that is morally wrong, and that these constraints remain in place even if by committing that immoral action we would prevent further similar immorality from occurring. For example, imagine we are confronted by a gunman who is intent on murdering three innocent people. In his perversity he bargains with us that if we undertake the murder of a fourth innocent person, he will reprieve the other three. What do we do? If we take up his offer, we will save three lives, but only by killing an innocent. The deontologist will be constrained by the rule that we should not commit murder, because murder is considered by her to be self-evidently wrong. However, if one murder is wrong, is a triple murder not three times worse, and three times more worthy of the constraint? Here the paradox is clear: by obeying the rule we may, in fact, cause the rule to be broken even more profoundly. There are a number of answers to this, most of which turn on the notion that the rights of the fourth innocent individual are no less important than the rights of the other three, and only by respecting the rights of that individual can we ever hope to respect the rights of all.

Ross's approach is also, not without its problems. Critics object that in any given real-life situation there may be a clash of the self-evident duties he proposes, and the question arises: which one trumps the other? This approach also lacks any consideration of the consequences of an action when deciding its morality. This, however, is a criticism of all flavours of *deontology* and brings us to the second of the moral frameworks: *consequentialism*, where we consider, not the *rightness* of our actions, but the *good* of their consequences.

CONSEQUENTIALISM

In this approach "the permissibility of an action is determined by how good its consequences are." (16) In the case above, one murder versus three murders are the two potential outcomes. For the consequentialist it is, as they say, a no-brainer.

Historically, the best-known example of a consequentialist moral framework is that of Utilitarianism. This was a school of thought that owes its origins to the English philosophers Jeremy Bentham (1748-1832) and John Stuart Mill (1806-73) (fig. 3). (16) They argued that an action was permissible if, and only if, its consequences were morally maximally good, and, that one state of affairs was morally at least as good as another if, and only if, the total individual well-being (or utility) it includes is at least as great as the total individual well-being in the other. (16) In other words, we should do what maximises the overall good and increases the overall well-being, irrespective of what those actions are. This approach does require us to do some arithmetic, for we are expected to perform some form of moral calculation to help us determine which course of action would result in the greatest overall well-being.

Objections

Consequentialism is vulnerable to major criticisms that impact on the rights, well-being and safety of the individual, because fundamentally in this approach to morality the individual is often irrelevant in comparison with the herd. For example, a utilitarian

Figure 3. John Stuart Mill (1806-73). Photogravure illustration used in several of his 19th century books.

may argue that it is morally permissible to deceive, harm, torture, or even kill an individual if this will produce a sufficiently favourable outcome for everyone. Such a position may be summarised as: the ends can justify the means, no matter what form those means take.

This, however, is a rather simplistic reading of utilitarianism, and anyone holding with this philosophy is likely to counter by saying that if such an approach were adopted – i.e. the torture and killing of innocents for the greater good – then the greater good would not be served. Indeed, in a society where such things were allowed, people would be living in fear and would have an overall reduction in their quality of life. Thus, they would argue that this sort of scenario, would not be justified by a utilitarian approach. However, on paper at least, it might be, and even such considered utilitarians would concede that in extreme circumstances it could, and indeed should, be the case.

VIRTUE THEORY

On some readings of the above two approaches it might be thought that both *deontology* and *consequentialism* are formulaic – simply follow the rule or rules, or simply do the calculation to determine which option offers the greatest good. In the words of LaFollette: "Ethics thus seems to resemble math." (17) Where are human judgement and wisdom in deciding what is morally permissible? Do these human attributes have no place? *Virtue theory* - the third and oldest of the three moral frameworks we are examining – offers them a home. This was the approach favoured by the Ancient Greeks. Indeed, it was formally laid out by Aristotle (fig. 4) in his Nicomachean Ethics, but it is also evident in the teachings of Buddha and Confucius. (18)

Figure 4. Aristotle (384-322 BCE). Marble bust, Roman copy after a Greek bronze original by Lysippos from 330 BCE. (Ludovisi Collection, National Museum of Rome – Palazzo Altemps, Rome, Italy.)

Here we are asked to consider the character of the doer, rather than any innate feature of the action, or its consequences. For someone to live a good or worthwhile life he or she must have virtues. These virtues include such things as benevolence, righteousness, courage and trustworthiness.

We do not have to follow specific rules, but should with the wisdom born of experience judge how to act. This experience will consist of specific examples of the virtues in action. As Hursthouse notes: "When, guided by Aristotle, we really take on board just how many different factors should be taken into account when we act and how they will vary with the circumstances, we see…that it is utterly implausible to suppose that such complexities could be catered for by usable rules or principles." (18) In order to determine if an action is morally permissible a virtue theorist need only ask if this is what a fully virtuous person would do in the same set of circumstances.

Objections

Two of the major objections to this approach are outlined by Annas. (19) She notes that *virtue theory* is alleged to be "too vague for us to apply it to the actual world", and because it depends on our personal understanding of virtue, which will be defined at least in part by our culture and social context, it will be necessarily "parochial in a way unsuitable for ethical thinking". *Virtue theory* is, however, unlike *deontology* or *consequentialism*, in that it is not setting out to offer us a formula for always doing the right thing. Rather it recognises that we have to work harder than this as individuals, and that "moral life is not static; it is always developing. When it comes to working out the right thing to do, we cannot shift the work to a theory, however excellent, because we, unlike the theories, are always learning, and so we are always aspiring to do better." (19)

You will find, if you choose to delve into the philosophical literature, many other versions of the three moral frameworks briefly described here, for this is a very active area of research, comment and debate. As indeed it should be, for working out how we decide right from wrong is at the very core of what it means to be human.

Before we move on, in the subsequent chapters, to look at historical examples that may shed light on this subject, it is worth returning for a moment to the application of these themes in practice. While there are many ethical decision points in the conduct of clinical research, none is more obvious than the evaluation of a study proposal by a Research Ethics Committee.

RESEARCH ETHICS COMMITTEES

A Research Ethics Committee (REC) is a group appointed to review research proposals in order to assess formally if that research is ethical. (20) Thus, these committees are charged with deciding what is morally permissible in the context of clinical research. REC review is an essential component of the modern research process, and although it necessarily happens behind closed doors, the decision-making processes inherent in delivering an ethical opinion, favourable or otherwise, are worthy of discussion. How do they reach such a decision? Which, if any, of the moral frameworks we have discussed do they adopt?

This is not the straightforward question it might seem, for RECs are convened as independent bodies – "independent of the researchers, the organisation funding the research and the organisation where the research will take place." (21) In the UK they do have guidelines to follow and standard operating procedures. But, when we examine the standard operating procedures for such committees produced by the National Research Ethics Service in the UK we find that most of the procedural instructions are concerned with the mechanics of how the committee should receive and process applications. (20) In contrast, there is almost nothing to direct the actual decision making processes of the committee members; nothing to tell them how to decide whether a proposal is ethical or not. They are referred to a related governance arrangements document, which notes that, "the research must conform to recognised ethical standards, which includes respecting the dignity, rights, safety and well-being of the people who take part." (21)

Of the three moral frameworks above we can immediately dismiss *consequentialism* as a contender for how RECs work. This approach is one that has not found favour in the field of clinical research. One of the principles of Good Clinical Practice states: "The rights, safety and well-being of the trial subjects shall prevail over the interests of science and society." (See appendix 3) The guidelines to which RECs adhere, vague though they are, do reiterate the need to consider the individual's dignity, rights, safety and well-being over those of the researchers or of the research itself. (21) This suggests that our concerns should primarily be with the individual without consideration of any greater good. Similarly, the charge to respect an individual's autonomy, which is a feature of many other moral frameworks, would be largely ignored by adopting a utilitarian approach to our moral decision making.

Could *virtue theory* underpin their operation? The guidelines for composition of RECs do note that "individuals of sound judgement, relevant experience and adequate training..." be sought for membership. (21) Thus, the members of a REC are chosen, at least partly, on the basis of their perceived virtues. The relative lack of specific decision making guidance that they are offered forces them to rely on their intuitive moral functions, and to make decisions without redress to some explicit moral algorithm. Perhaps, then, RECs are expected to work within a framework of *virtue theory* whereby their experience and their possession of the virtues will see them through.

This is, however, not the whole story, for although there is no explicit moral algorithm laid out for the REC members to follow they are giving some direction. Specifically, "RECs are expected to reflect the currency of ethical debate." (21) They are also expected to consider each proposal against a set of standards, without, it must be added, being told what those standards are, other than that they should uphold the dignity, rights, safety and well-being of the study participants.

Thus, while they could not be said to be adhering to a hard Kantian line in their deontology, they may be deontologists none the less, acting more in accord with Ross's softer approach, where a range of self-evident moral duties are to be considered within a complex context that is specific for each proposal.

CONCLUSION

Julia Annas noted above that "moral life is not static" – nor, we might argue, is the moral landscape. New developments in science and technology, new possibilities previously undreamt of and changing social norms all have an impact on the way we think about bio-ethics.

Kant's moral absolutism, is in some ways comforting against these winds of change, but the flexibility offered by other approaches, such as Ross's *deontology* or even *virtue theory*, allows us the possibility of bending in those winds. Bending – but with our feet firmly on moral grounds.

REFERENCES

1. Singer P. *Ethics*. Oxford University Press, Oxford, 1994.
2. McNaughton D and Rawling P. Deontology. In: *Ethics in Practice. An Anthology*, LaFollette H (Ed) 3rd Edition, Blackwell Publishing, Oxford, 2007.
3. Gewirth A. The golden rule rationalised. In: *Ethical Theory. An Anthology*. Shafer-Landau R (Ed) Blackwell Publishing, Oxford, 2007.
4. Luke 6:31.
5. Confucius. *The Analects*. XV.23, Waley A (Trans). Everyman's Library, Alfred A. Knopf, New York, 2000.
6. *The Mahabharata*, Book 13: Anusasana Parva Section CXIII. Ganguli KM (Trans). http://www.mahabharataonline.com/translation/maha bharata_13b078.php [Accessed: 27 July, 2010].
7. *Farewell Sermon*, Muhammad. http://www.islamicity.com/mosque/lastserm.HTM [Accessed: 27 July, 2010].
8. *The Dhammapada*, Chapter 10. Punishment. Fronsdal G. (Trans) http://www.holyebooks.org/budhism/ dhammapada.html [Accessed: 27 July, 2010].
9. Leviticus 19:18.
10. Hippocrates. *The Corpus*. Kaplan Publishing, New York, 2008.
11. Smith CM. Origin and uses of primum non nocere-above all, do no harm! *Journal of Clinical Pharmacology* 2005; 45: 371-7.
12. Kant I. *Groundwork of the Metaphysic of Morals*. In: *The Moral Law*, Paton HJ. Hutchison University Library, London, 1972.
13. Ross W D. 1930. *The Right and the Good*. Reprinted with an introduction by Philip Stratton-Lake. Oxford University Press, Oxford, 2002.

14. National Commission for the Protection of Human Subjects of Biomedical and Behavioral Research. *The Belmont Report Ethical Principles and Guidelines for the protection of human subjects of research.* http://ohsr.od.nih.gov/guidelines/belmont.html [Accessed: 28 July, 2010].

15. Nozick R. *Anarchy, State and Utopia.* Blackwell Publishing, Malden, 1974.

16. Vallentyne P. Consequentialism. In: *Ethics in Practice. An Anthology*, LaFollette H (Ed) 3rd Edition, Blackwell Publishing, Oxford, 2007.

17. LaFollette H. Theorizing about Ethics. In: *Ethics in Practice. An Anthology*, LaFollette H (Ed) 3rd Edition, Blackwell Publishing, Oxford, 2007.

18. Hursthouse R. Virtue Theory. In: *Ethics in Practice. An Anthology*, LaFollette H (Ed) 3rd Edition, Blackwell Publishing, Oxford, 2007.

19. Annas J. Being virtuous and doing the right thing. In: *Ethical Theory. An Anthology.* Shafer-Landau R (Ed) Blackwell Publishing, Oxford, 2007.

20. NRES. *Standard Operating Procedures for Research Ethics Committees* v4.0. National Patient Safety Agency, 2009. http://www.nres.npsa.nhs.uk/news-and-publications/ publications/standard-operating-procedures/[Accessed: 29 July, 2010].

21. UK Departments of Health. *Governance arrangements for research ethics committees. A Proposed harmonised edition.* Department of Health, 2009. http://www.nres.npsa.nhs.uk/news-and-publications/ news/harmonised-gafrec-consultation/ [Accessed: 29 July, 2010].

2

"From a regard to truth"

James Lind and the implementation of research findings

When patients agree to take part in clinical trials there is a moral contract, albeit implicit, that their involvement and their sacrifice will be rewarded by consequent improvements in medical practice, built upon the findings of the study. The honouring of this moral contract and the repayment of the ensuing debt is usually in the form of publication and dissemination of the research findings at the end of the study. However, this is only a partial repayment. For the contract to be wholly fulfilled medical practice has to change to reflect any relevant new findings. If this does not happen we must ask why, and we must question the ethics of such an incomplete conclusion to the research process.

The implementation of research findings into clinical practice is, however, not a simple task and is one that has many obstacles and barriers to its completion. This is true today, but was equally true more than 250 years ago and is exemplified by the story of the Scottish Naval Surgeon, James Lind.

BACKGROUND

From the mid-16th century, countless sailors from around the world took to the seas on long intercontinental voyages. Months, often years, were spent away from land, for international trade or naval warfare. For the vast majority, on board conditions were extremely poor. The ships were hugely over-crowded and provisions were limited by the practicalities of storing and preserving food over many months at sea. A standard sailor's diet included salt beef or pork, dried fish, hard tack or biscuit, butter, cheese, peas and beer. (1) Such a restricted diet over many months at sea led to deficiency diseases amongst the men, most notably scurvy - the consequence of vitamin C deficiency.

SCURVY

Scurvy was a major health problem throughout the age of sail, but historians differ in their estimates of its impact. Some claim that more than 2 million sailors perished from the ravages of this disease; a number greater than those killed by storms, shipwreck and combat combined. (1) However, others claim that diseases such as typhus may have confounded these figures. (2) Whatever the exact numbers it was a deadly constant and greatly feared by sailors. One account, illustrating the extent of scurvy's brutality, details Lord Anson's epic journey around the world. In 1740, while Britain was at war with Spain, he led a fleet of six warships and almost 2,000 sailors on a circumnavigation of the globe. Four years later, Anson returned with just one ship and

Figure 1. James Lind commemorative plaque from Edinburgh University Medical School placed there in 1953 by grateful citrus fruit growers from California and Arizona (photograph courtesy of Iain Milne, RCPE Library).

188 men, with reports that scurvy was responsible for 997 of the deaths. (3) Such an account was not rare. Indeed, during the Seven Years' War with France, of almost 185,000 sailors, more than 133,000 died of disease, and the majority of these were attributable to scurvy. Only 1,512 were believed killed in action. (4)

TREATMENTS

However, not all voyages resulted in such tragic losses due to scurvy. Almost 150 years before Anson's voyage around the world, there was an outbreak of scurvy as Vasco da Gama made the long voyage from Portugal to Asia. It was observed that the ill were relieved by citrus fruits. (5) Furthermore, in 1601 James Lancaster set off on a three-year voyage to the Spice Islands and used lemon juice to stave off scurvy aboard one of the four ships under his command. By administering 3 spoonfuls of lemon juice to the 202 sailors on board the *Red Dragon*, it was noted that he had "cured many of his men and preserved the rest." (1, 5)

It would appear that, by the early 17th century, a means to prevent and cure scurvy had already been identified by the keen observational skills of sailors. Unfortunately, the situation was greatly confused by a plethora of theories about scurvy, and its potential cures, from the eminent physicians of the day. Unlike those who advocated citrus fruits, many of the well-regarded physicians had never actually seen a man with scurvy and based the entirety of their recommendations on the prevailing medical theories. Unfortunately, those who believed in the benefits of oranges and lemons could not explain their mechanism of action. Thus, despite their efficacy, the Admiralty chose instead to implement the bizarre therapies proposed by others which were, theoretically, entirely plausible in the context of 17th century medicine.

Such therapies included sea-water, vinegar, oil of vitriol (dilute sulphuric acid) and malt wort (a sweetened soaked malt extract). (1)

LIND'S CONTRIBUTION

With the benefits of citrus fruits practically forgotten, scurvy continued to rage through the ships during the early 18th century. Many therapies were recommended without proof of their efficacy until, in 1747, a young Scottish surgeon aboard the *HMS Salisbury* attempted to clarify the situation. James Lind (fig. 1) was acutely aware of the impact of scurvy and the urgency with which a solution was required, when he said:

> *the scurvy alone, during the last war, proved a more destructive enemy, and cut off more valuable lives, than the united efforts of the French and Spanish arms.*(6)

Six weeks after leaving port, on the last of six patrols of the Channel, Lind conducted what has since become his world famous clinical trial.

> *On the 20th of May, 1747, I took twelve patients in the scurvy, on board the Salisbury at sea. Their cases were as similar as I could have them. They all in general had putrid gums, the spots and lassitude, with weakness of their knees. ... and had one diet common to all... Two of these were ordered each a quart of cyder a-day. Two others took twenty-five gutts of elixir vitriol three times a-day.... Two others took two spoonfuls of vinegar three times a-day...; Two of the worst patients...were put under a course of sea-water... Two others had each two oranges and one lemon given them every day. These they ate with greediness, at different times upon an empty stomach. They continued but six days under this course, having the quantity that could be spared. The two remaining patients took the bigness of a nutmeg three times a-day.... The consequence was, that the most sudden and visible good effects were perceived from*

> *the use of oranges and lemons; one of those who had taken them,*
> *being at the end of six days fit for duty…. The other was the best*
> *recovered of any in his condition; and being now deemed pretty well,*
> *was appointed nurse to the rest of the sick.* (6)

His results were conclusive. By using a set of carefully conducted, controlled clinical experiments Lind was able to demonstrate that those who ate citrus fruits recovered, while those who took other standard therapies of the time did not. His experiments clarified the situation and seemed to address the confusion caused by the many unfounded recommendations that hampered the management of scurvy.

In 1748, Lind left the Navy and returned to Edinburgh where he completed his MD in venereal disease. He began working as a physician and five years later published the findings of his experiments in his *Treatise on The Scurvy, Containing an Inquiry into the Nature, Causes, and Cure, of That Disease Together with a Critical and Chronological View on What Has Been Published on the Subject* (fig. 2). (6)

Importantly, in his book, Lind first undertook a review of the literature. By critically appraising previously published works he attempted to address the deficiencies in the many theories, which acted as barriers to the effective treatment of scurvy. He recognised that "it was necessary to remove a great deal of rubbish" but insisted,

> *where I have been necessarily led, in this disagreeable part of the*
> *work, to criticise the sentiments of eminent and learned authors, I*
> *have not done it with a malignant view of depreciating their labours,*
> *or their names; but from a regard to truth, and the good of mankind.*
> (6)

He published the findings of his experiments and offered his conclusions in 1753. However, it was not until 1795 – the year after Lind's death - that the Admiralty began the routine issue of lemon juice to their sailors for the prevention of scurvy.

Viewed from a 21st century perspective it seems inexplicable that a cure for a serious and highly prevalent disease should be conclusively demonstrated, yet not implemented for over 40 years. However, when attempting to translate clinical research findings into practice a number of barriers must first be overcome.

BARRIERS TO IMPLEMENTATION IN THE 18TH CENTURY

In Lind's case, personal and professional credibility may have contributed to his failure to convince the Admiralty to adopt his method of preventing scurvy as routine practice. Although the publication of his *Treatise on The Scurvy* made his reputation and allowed his appointment as director of the new Navy hospital at Haslar in 1758, unlike his contemporaries, he began life in the Navy as a lowly surgeon's mate, having come from a family without influential connections. Perhaps had he a higher social standing it may not have taken 42 years for the recommendations of his *Treatise* to be implemented. For example, Gilbert Blane, a Scottish physician from an upper class family, Physician to the Fleet and later Commissioner on the Board of the Sick and Wounded Sailors, was subsequently instrumental in the introduction of daily rationing of lemon juice for all sailors in 1795.

However, there were a number of other reasons that contributed to this delay. Although Lind demonstrated that oranges and lemons were effective in curing scurvy, he did not appreciate that a lack of one of their key constituents was its cause, nor their mechanism of action. Lind believed that the acids of oranges and lemons had some special quality, and hence their efficacy over

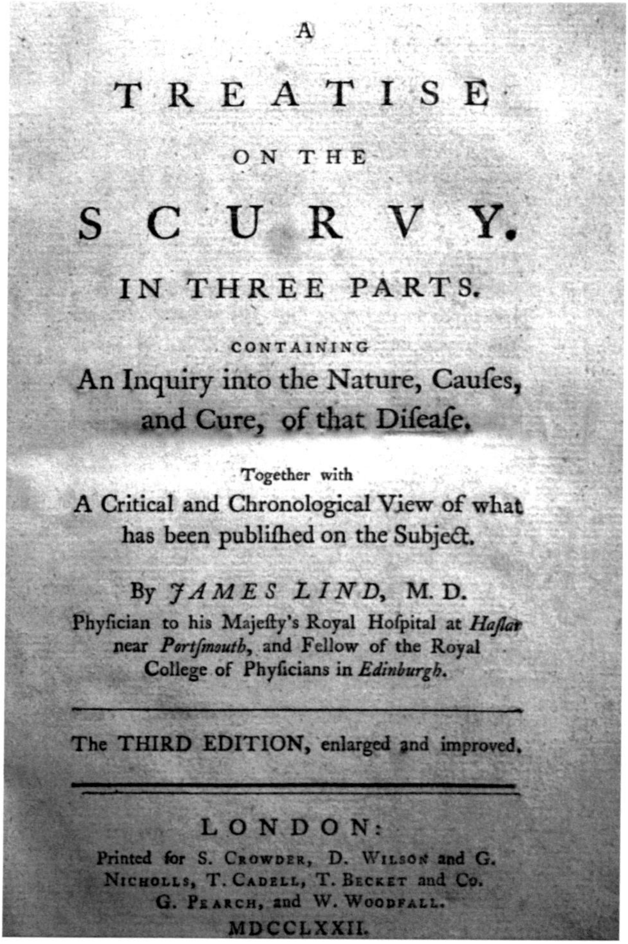

A

TREATISE

ON THE

SCURVY.

IN THREE PARTS.

CONTAINING

An Inquiry into the Nature, Caufes, and Cure, of that Difeafe.

Together with
A Critical and Chronological View of what has been publifhed on the Subject.

By *JAMES LIND*, M.D.
Phyfician to his Majefty's Royal Hofpital at *Haflar* near *Portfmouth*, and Fellow of the Royal College of Phyficians in *Edinburgh*.

The THIRD EDITION, enlarged and improved.

LONDON:
Printed for S. CROWDER, D. WILSON and G. NICHOLLS, T. CADELL, T. BECKET and Co. G. PEARCH, and W. WOODFALL.
MDCCLXXII.

Figure 2. Frontispiece from Lind's *Treatise on The Scurvy*. (Courtesy of The Royal College of Physicians and Surgeons of Glasgow, photograph by the authors.)

vinegar and oil of vitriol, which were standard therapies at the time.

He also recognised that the practicalities of transporting enough fresh fruit for many hundreds of sailors on long voyages lacked feasibility. He therefore recommended a method by which the "virtues of twelve dozen lemons or oranges, may be put into a quart-bottle and preserved for years." (1) His proposed method involved concentrating lemon juice into a "rob" by heating it and unknowingly depleting its vitamin C content. Although some vitamin C would have been preserved in the "rob", it was a concentrate and given in small doses, meaning that it was ineffective. The "rob" was expensive to produce and given its inert nature, it was perhaps not surprising that this recommendation was not adopted aboard Navy vessels.

What was surprising, however, was that having undertaken his previous study with such scientific rigour, Lind proposed his "rob" without evidence of its efficacy – an approach he had derided others for in his literature review on scurvy. Had he been consistent in his methodology, he might have developed an understanding of the mechanism of action of citrus fruits, and been able to make a more informed recommendation.

Finally, not only did Lind hail from a humble background but also, by strongly criticising the theories and recommendations of the most eminent physicians of the day, he may have alienated them. Thus, his own recommendations may not have received the necessary support from the very physicians he openly attacked.

BARRIERS TO IMPLEMENTATION TODAY

Clinical research provides innovative interventions aimed at delivering a better quality of care to patients. However, for clinical research to be truly successful its legacy must last beyond the discovery and development of something new – it must be effectively implemented into daily practice.

While issues specific to the naval hierarchy and medical theory of the day would have contributed to Lind's difficulties, the implementation of research into clinical practice is a problem that exists to this day. (7)

Seven obvious barriers may be noted:

- Poor or incomplete communication of research findings
- Lack of credibility of the research team
- Perceived poor quality of the research
- Costly resource implications of implementation
- Unfavourable socio-political backdrop
- Presence of vested interests in the medical community and/or policy makers
- Resistance to any form of change from the status quo.

As we have seen above, Lind met with all these barriers and did not live to see the implementation of his research findings. But, this is not simply a symptom of the past, and even today these barriers are still in place, often requiring considerable efforts to overcome. For example, in 1984, Barry J Marshall and Robin Warren demonstrated that *Helicobacter pylori* was a bacterial pathogen implicated in the pathogenesis of peptic ulcer disease. The implications of this finding for medical and surgical practices were enormous. Peptic ulcer disease was thought to be an incurable disease caused by stress, poor diet and alcohol. Marshall and Warren showed that, in fact, *H. pylori* was responsible and sufferers could be cured with antibiotics. With millions affected worldwide, they pursued the implementation of their findings with urgency. However, despite having proved the efficacy of antibiotics in the treatment of peptic ulcer disease, many dismissed their claims and it took ten years before their evidence was finally accepted, and another ten before they were awarded the Nobel Prize for their work. (8) Marshall noted that he had to convince even himself that this was not "just a very strange infection that was occurring in Perth, Western Australia perhaps from Wombats or Kangaroos" suggesting that there was a significant credibility barrier that he and his colleague had to overcome. (9)

Even when the credibility of the research team and the quality of the data are not in doubt there may still be significant delays. For example, in 1994 it was conclusively demonstrated that cholesterol lowering statin therapy reduced all cause mortality in those patients who had established coronary heart disease. (10) However, in a survey of clinical practice in England in 2002 less than half of patients with this disease even had their cholesterol levels checked, with a much smaller number on statin treatment. (11) Resource issues and institutional inertia were overcome only in 2004 when the new General Medical Services contract for primary care physicians offered financial incentives for the identification and treatment of such patients. (12)

ETHICAL DIMENSIONS

Much has been written about the ethics of clinical research. Most focusses on the design and conduct of studies, with ethical principles guiding these aspects of research to protect patients from harm. However, a wider ethical perspective is also needed, that looks beyond the trial itself.

It is regarded as imperative that research findings, irrespective of the outcome, should be published and disseminated to the medical community. (13) To do otherwise is considered not only bad practice, but also immoral. Clinical trials inevitably put study participants at risk, and utilise often scarce research resources that are subject to fierce competition. If we conduct a trial without producing any useful product in the form of published findings, we have squandered those resources and exposed our study participants to unnecessary risks without any balancing benefits. Furthermore, it may be argued that a research team not only has a moral obligation to publish and disseminate their findings, but also to seek the implementation of those findings into clinical practice. This, of course, can often only be through facilitation and lobbying as researchers are rarely also policy makers.

As we have seen above, for an important and clinically relevant research finding to be translated into practice a number of obstacles must be overcome. Not all of these are amenable to the research team, but their voices can be a force that helps breech these barriers. Thus, to view the research process as complete on the publication of the results is to leave the job only partially done. We have a moral obligation to go further and to act as the best advocates of our own work. What begins with the presentation and publication of results in peer-reviewed journals should continue with researchers being active participants in the debate about their work, its implications and, if appropriate, its implementation. Good communication between researchers and key stakeholders is therefore essential for the successful implementation of research. (14)

CONCLUSION

James Lind continued to work on scurvy in the years following his landmark trial, but despite his best efforts the barriers to implementation of his findings were too great, and could only be overcome by the collective efforts of others.

Perhaps recognising the difficulties inherent in the implementation of research findings, Lind himself noted, four years after the publication of his *Treatise*:

> *The province has been mine to deliver precepts: the power is in others to execute.* (15)

While this may have been an entirely appropriate approach in the highly hierarchical medical and social structures of the 18th century, it is not necessarily one that we should adopt today.

REFERENCES

1. Bown, S. *Scurvy: How a Surgeon, a Mariner and a Gentleman Solved the Greatest Medical Mystery of the Age of the Sail.* Summersdale, Chichester, 2003.
2. Wootten D. Postscript 2007. In: *Bad Medicine: Doctors Doing Harm Since Hippocrates.* Oxford University Press, Oxford, 2007.
3. Watt J. The medical bequest of disaster at sea: Commodore Anson's circumnavigation 1740–44. *Journal of the Royal College of Physicians London.* 1998; 32: 572–9.
4. Northcote, W. The Diseases Incident to Armies, with the Method of Cure, Translated from the Original of Baron Van Swieten, to Which Are Added the Nature and Treatment of Gun-shot Wounds, by John Ranby. Likewise Some Brief Directions to be Followed by Sea Surgeons in Engagements. Also preventatives of the scurvy at sea. Published for the use of military, and naval surgeons in America. R Bell, Philadelphia, 1776: 167.
5. Baron JH. Sailors' scurvy before and after James Lind – a reassessment. *Nutrition Reviews* 2009; 67: 315-32.
6. Lind J. *A Treatise of the Scurvy in Three Parts. Containing an Inquiry into the Nature, Causes and Cure of that Disease, together with a Critical and Chronological View of what has been published on the subject.* A Miller, Edinburgh, 1753.
7. Grol R, Grimshaw J. From best evidence to best practice: effective implementation of change. *Lancet* 2003; 362: 1225-30.

8.   Barry J. Marshall - Autobiography. Nobelprize.org. http://nobelprize.org/nobel_prizes/medicine/laureates/2005/marshall-autobio.html [Accessed: 17 June 2010]

9.   Barry J. Marshall - Nobel Lecture. Nobelprize.org. http://nobelprize.org/nobel_prizes/medicine/laureates/2005/marshall-lecture.html [Accessed: 17 June 2010]

10. Scandinavian Simvastatin Survival Study Group. Randomized trial of cholesterol lowering in 4444 patients with coronary heart disease: the Scandinavian Simvastatin Survival Study. *Lancet* 1994; 344: 1383–9.

11. de Lusignan S, Dzregah B, Hague N, Chan T. Cholesterol management in patients with ischaemic heart disease: an audit based appraisal of progress towards clinical targets in primary care. *British Journal of Cardiology* 2003; 10: 223–8.

12. Shekelle P. New contract for general practitioners. *British Medical Journal*. 2003; 326: 457–8.

13. Rennie D. The Obligation to Publish and Disseminate Results. In: *The Oxford Textbook of Clinical Research Ethics*. Emanuel EJ, Lie RK, Grady C, Miller FG, Crouch RA, Wendler D (Eds). Oxford University Press, Oxford, 2008.

14. Cohen DJ, Crabtree BF, Etz RS, et al. Fidelity versus flexibility: translating evidence-based research into practice. *American Journal of Preventive Medicine* 2008; 35: S381–9.

15. Lind, J. *An Essay on the Most Effectual Means of preserving the Health of Seamen in the Royal Navy*. London, 1757.

3

"Obey, suffer and comply"

William Beaumont and the research relationship

BACKGROUND

The relationship between individuals who conduct clinical research and those who take part is at the very centre of the research process. Indeed, the very words we use to describe those individuals who take part are revealing: *patients*, *subjects*, *participants* or *volunteers*. These terms are often used interchangeably, but they are not necessarily synonymous and may reveal much about the nature of the research relationship, which should be one of partnership rather than subjugation. Clinical research should not be done *to* people, but *with* people. (1)

One element of this relationship, which bears close examination, is that of payment. If those who participate are financially compensated a number of ethical issues are raised. One historical example where both the research relationship and the issue of compensation are central to the story is that of Dr William Beaumont and his patient Alexis St. Martin (figs 1 and 2).

A SHOOTING ACCIDENT

On 6 June 1822, Alexis St. Martin, a young French Canadian, was badly injured by a misfired shotgun whilst working as a voyageur, or canoeist, for the American Fur Company at Fort Mackinac, Michigan territory. The surgeon who attended him was William Beaumont. He recounts:

> *I was called to him immediately after the incident. Found …[a] protrusion resembling a portion of the stomach, which at first sight I could not believe possible to be that organ in that situation with the subject surviving, but on closer examination I found it to be actually the stomach with a puncture in the protruding portion large enough to receive my forefinger… I considered any attempt to save life entirely useless.* (2)

Thus, Beaumont regarded the prognosis to be hopeless, but nevertheless he treated and dressed the wound. Against the odds St. Martin survived and over the following months steadily grew stronger. However, despite the best efforts of his physician his wound healed incompletely, leaving a patent gastric fistula or open passageway between the inside of the stomach and the body surface. Despite his return to relative health St. Martin was unable to take up his previous occupation and the local authorities, keen to relieve themselves of the burden of his care, planned to repatriate him to Canada.

Figure I. Dr. William Beaumont (1785-1853) from a painting by Chester Harding. (Courtesy of the National Library of Medicine, IHM.)

Figure 2. Alexis St. Martin (1797-1880) aged 67. (Courtesy of the National Library of Medicine, IHM.)

Knowing that St. Martin was unfit for the journey and recognising his patient as a unique opportunity for study, Beaumont objected and took St. Martin into his home as a servant. He continued to treat St. Martin and by the end of the second year he had resumed a practically normal life. His unusual patent gastric fistula, however, remained. Beaumont noted:

> *I can look directly into the cavity of the stomach...observe its motion, and almost see the process of digestion...The case affords an excellent opportunity for experiment upon the gastric fluids and the process of digestion.* (2) (fig. 3)

Clearly, Beaumont had decided to take advantage of this opportunity and he soon began conducting experiments on St. Martin. Beaumont describes how he:

> *Suspended flesh, raw or roasted, and other substances in the hole to ascertain the length of time required to digest each...*(3)

With these early experiments Beaumont quickly realised that he lacked the necessary scientific knowhow to pursue his work effectively. He had no formal medical education and, at Fort Mackinac, felt isolated from his more experienced contemporaries. He wrote to his friend, the US Surgeon-General, requesting that he might be stationed somewhere he could get the mentorship he needed. Meanwhile, St. Martin was increasingly unhappy. Although physically fit again, he found himself entrapped in a difficult dependent relationship with Beaumont. St. Martin was at the constant disposal of Beaumont and, despite receiving food and lodgings, he wanted to escape.

After some time, the order came for Beaumont to move to Fort Niagara where he could seek the advice he required to conduct his experiments with confidence. On 1 August 1825, Beaumont began his first formal series of experiments.

At twelve o'clock, A.M., I introduced through the perforation into the stomach the following articles of diet, suspended by a silk string, and fastened at proper distances so as to pass in without pain - viz.: a piece of high-seasoned a la mode beef; *a piece of* raw, salted, fat pork; *a piece of* raw, salted lean beef; *a piece* of boiled, salted beef; *a piece of* stale bread; *and a bunch of* raw, sliced cabbage. (4)

Every hour the foodstuffs were removed and inspected until, after four hours, St. Martin was in such discomfort that the experiment was stopped. A few days later Beaumont conducted further experiments, fasting St. Martin for 17 hours before recording the temperature of the stomach using a thermometer inserted through his fistula – which St. Martin found particularly unpleasant. (4)

It was clear that St. Martin was not fully eager to participate in such experiments. Historians suggest that St. Martin was, in fact, profoundly unhappy at this time but that Beaumont was "too indifferent to his servant's psychology, too absorbed in the experiments that had suddenly become the meaning of his life, to worry what so low an individual might be thinking."(5) Such was St. Martin's discontent that, when the two men arrived in Plattsburg following a trip through upper New York State, St. Martin took advantage of their proximity to Canada and, with Beaumont asleep, he gathered his belongings and left. Later, Beaumont described how St. Martin "returned to Canada, his native place, without obtaining my consent."(4) Interestingly, this is the only mention of consent in his subsequent book of over 300 pages.

Bitterly disappointed, Beaumont tried desperately to locate St. Martin. Not only did he recognise he had lost a great opportunity to improve the scientific understanding of digestion, but he feared that if he did not further experiment on St. Martin it was only a matter of time before someone else would, and with

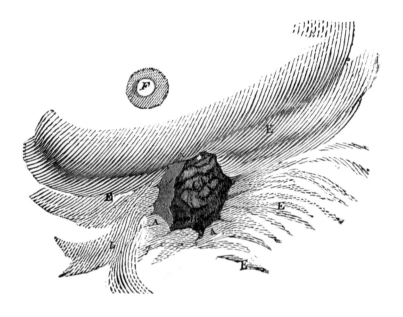

Figure 3. Engraving from Dr William Beaumont's work: *Experiments and Observations on the Gastric Juice and the Physiology of Digestion*, 1833. (Courtesy of The Royal College of Physicians and Surgeons of Glasgow, photograph by the authors.)

that he would forego the celebrity St. Martin's study might afford him.

Eventually, word of his whereabouts reached Beaumont and after much negotiation St. Martin, who was now married with children, was reunited with Beaumont in the summer of 1829. Beaumont was pleased to find that his subject's condition had not changed, commenting that his "stomach and side were in similar condition as when he left me in 1825." (4) However, this time St. Martin was accompanied by his wife who gave him much needed encouragement and support. Whilst this certainly improved St. Martin's morale, it caused further friction between the two men.

Over the next two years, Beaumont conducted many experiments observing the effects of different variables such as the weather and emotion on the process of digestion and the conditions in which gastric juice can function. At the end of 1831, Beaumont decided to travel to Europe with St. Martin where he could study, in greater detail, the chemical make-up of gastric juice. In 1832, before leaving for Paris, Beaumont allowed St. Martin to accompanied his family to Canada, but fearing St. Martin may once again try to escape, Beaumont compiled a legal document and insisted that St. Martin, who could not read or write, sign it. (6) By marking an 'X' at the bottom of the contract, St. Martin agreed that in return for board, lodging, clothes and US$ 150 he would:

> *submit to, assist, and promote by all means in his power such physiological or medical experiments as said William shall direct or cause to be made on or in the stomach of him, the said Alexis, either through or by the means of aperture or opening thereto in the side of him, the said Alexis, or otherwise, and will obey, suffer, and comply with all reasonable and proper orders or experiments of the said William in relation thereto, and in relation to the exhibiting and showing of his said stomach and the powers and properties thereof,*

and the appurtenances, and powers, properties, situation, and state of the contents thereof. (2)

St. Martin did return but because of time constraints the intended trip to Europe never took place.

Having learned from his past experiences Beaumont was keen to keep St. Martin under his care and in December 1832 St. Martin was enlisted in the army. In doing so, it is likely that Beaumont aimed to compensate for the cost of providing for his patient whilst further restricting the freedom of St. Martin. Unlike before, any attempt by St. Martin to escape would now be seen as desertion and therefore could result in harsh punishment. (6) St. Martin had little authority and, without the support of his family, submitted daily to numerous experiments. He was deeply depressed and drank heavily.

In 1833, Beaumont completed and published his book entitled *Experiments and Observations on the Gastric Juice, and the Physiology of Digestion* (fig. 4). (4) It was well received by the scientific community and he received many requests to display and demonstrate his subject. Such requests further depressed St. Martin as he deeply resented being exhibited by Beaumont as a scientific curiosity. Being so obviously miserable, it appears Beaumont felt some pity for his subject and allowed him two months leave to return to his family in Canada. However, fearful that he may not return, he made St. Martin sign a new contract lasting a further two years worth US$200 per annum.

St. Martin never returned. In June 1834 he wrote that his wife wished him to remain in Canada: "I am much obliged to you for what you have done and if it was in my power I should do all I could for you with pleasure." (6) After 238 recorded experiments over the course of 10 years, St. Martin's research relationship with Beaumont had ended. In subsequent years Beaumont offered St. Martin increasing financial incentives and assurances that he could depend on his "liberality and justice" should he return, but to no avail. (6)

St. Martin lived to an old age, dying in 1880, 27 years after the death of Beaumont. After St. Martin's death, the eminent physician, Sir William Osler offered his family money to conduct an autopsy. Despite their poverty they refused, preferring to allow St. Martin to rest in peace. To further thwart any further experimentation they allowed his body to decompose such that it had to be left outside the church during his funeral service and they arranged for his corpse to be buried eight rather than six feet deep to protect against grave robbers. (5)

RESEARCH RELATIONSHIPS

The nature and balance of the research relationship, varies widely from study to study. In some, there is extreme coercion imposed by a powerful investigator and an impotent subject. An obvious example of this would be the relationship between Nazi doctors and their concentration camp inmates during the Second World War. (7)

In many other studies there is something much more akin to a conventional doctor-patient relationship – not necessarily equal, but nonetheless built upon mutual respect. Finally, in some studies there may be a true partnership between the investigator and the volunteer, where the study participant is viewed as a vital member of the study team.

Certain research relationships can be problematic and bring into question the morality of the study in question. These are predominantly ones where a power relationship exists between the investigator and the subject that may unduly influence the latter's participation in the study. For example, a student who is concerned about her grades may feel the need to consent to be a healthy volunteer in her professor's study; an employee may feel

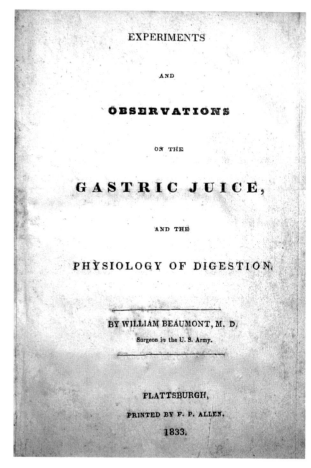

Figure 4. Frontispiece of Beaumont's *Experiments and Observations on the Gastric Juice, and the Physiology of Digestion.* (Courtesy of The Royal College of Physicians and Surgeons of Glasgow, photograph by the authors.)

compelled to participate in his employer's trial in order to gain favour or avoid professional censure; a young soldier may take part in a research study conducted by a senior officer because it is unclear to him that it is not an order but a choice; and finally a prisoner may be powerless to resist the research study of the prison medical officer. In all these relationships the research subject is either fearful of the consequences of non-participation, induced by the professional prospects of participation or ignorant of the possibility of refusal.

When a research protocol is reviewed by an ethics committee one of the things they will examine is the nature of this research relationship. If, like the examples above, it is one based on power or patronage, the committee may question the freedom of the volunteers to make an informed choice and the overall ethics of such an approach. (8)

The relationship between Beaumont and St. Martin was complex and multi-layered. Initially, it was a simple doctor-patient interaction, but with time it developed into an investigator-research subject one. Further, because Beaumont was also St. Martin's employer, a power relationship existed between them of master and servant. And finally, with St. Martin's enlistment in the army he assumed an even more formally subservient role to Beaumont. The latter two are of particular importance for they impose serious constraints on St. Martin's freedom of choice. He would have believed, probably correctly, that failure to participate in Beaumont's studies would have consequences for his livelihood, and subsequently that refusal may have resulted in disciplinary proceedings.

Beaumont, thus, had a great deal of control over St. Martin. Indeed, years after he left Beaumont, St. Martin still felt his physician's power over him as he refused offers from other researchers wishing to experiment on him saying that he "was not his own master." (6)

RESEARCH VERSUS CARE

If the medical team responsible for the care of a patient is also the one conducting the research project in which that patient is invited to participate, there is potential for confusion. Research participants should be in no doubt that the procedures they are to undergo or the treatments they are to take are part of a research project and do not constitute their normal care. Any potential for confusion must be avoided and with it the possibility that a study participant's informed consent may be compromised. Indeed, when considering the content of both the informed consent discussion and the written informed consent form, the first recommendation of the International Conference on Harmonisation – Good Clinical Practice (ICH-GCP) guidelines is that we must state: "That the trial involves research." (9)

In the case of Beaumont his initial care of St. Martin slowly transformed into research. While, ultimately, St. Martin was surely not in any doubt that he was a research subject in a series of experiments it is not clear when this transition took place or whether St. Martin was fully aware, at least early on, where his treatment stopped and where the research began. To further complicate matters St. Martin may have felt that his continued care was conditional on his agreement to participate in Beaumont's research. Today this would be seen as a clear case of coercion and would be disallowed by an ethics committee. However, such an approach would not have raised any concern in the early 19th century.

MONEY

All clinical research carries risks to the participants. At one end of the spectrum these may be minor and easily quantifiable, while at the other end, serious and difficult, or even impossible, to define. The motivation for an individual to assume these risks can vary, whether as a healthy volunteer or as a patient with a disease of interest. Whilst altruism and a desire to aid scientific and medical progress may be key motivations for some (10), others may feel that the risks they undertake justify some form of compensation. Participants may receive this compensation simply in the form of money. Others may receive benefits such as free medical care, or access to otherwise unobtainable treatments.

St. Martin received compensation in turn for allowing Beaumont to conduct his experiments. He received a wage for his role as a servant in Beaumont's home as well as US$150 upon signing a contract in 1832 for his role as a research participant. In subsequent years Beaumont offered him contracts up to the value of US$500 to encourage him to return for further experimentation, but none of these were accepted. Whether or not St. Martin would have participated in the research without such financial compensation can be debated. Given his poverty and disability it is understandable that he should try to take full advantage of his situation to improve his life and that of his family. Certainly, after his return to Canada in late 1833, Beaumont intimated that he believed St. Martin's key purpose was "to extort a much higher salary." (6)

Payment of research subjects has a long history and probably goes back much further than Beaumont and St. Martin, but even today there is little consensus on its morality. (11) Although very different approaches apply in different countries it is, however, universally agreed that payment should not amount to "undue inducement." (12)

Thus, one of the central questions raised when we consider the payment of trial subjects is whether money acts as an undue inducement, which may therefore "blind people to risk?" (8) The limited evidence available would suggest that this is not necessarily the case. (13, 14) Interestingly, even in St. Martin's case, the offers of progressively larger payments were not a sufficient inducement to entice him back from Canada to Beaumont's research. An important and related question is whether financial payments act as undue inducements particularly for poor people who are thus disproportionately exploited in medical research. (15, 16) One legal representative of the family of a young man who died during a clinical trial noted: "This is not something you or I do. This is something the poor do so that the rich can get better drugs." (15)

St. Martin was poor. He was also young, illiterate and undoubtedly vulnerable. The money, board and lodgings he was offered by Beaumont early in their research relationship must have been an inducement to comply, although one on top of an already blurring doctor-patient relationship. Had St. Martin been a rich fur trader in the same situation it is tempting to speculate whether Beaumont would have had such an easy time.

CONCLUSION

Our current codes of practice governing the conduct of clinical trials aim to protect trial participants, especially those who are vulnerable. We are expected to define clearly the limits of clinical care and clinical research: to offer prospective participants appropriate information and to facilitate their free choice. We are not expected to coerce, induce or otherwise exert control over our subjects because of any position of power we, as investigators, may hold. In short we are not expected to treat those who take part in our trials as subjects, but rather as participants, and, at best, as members of our research team. Beaumont needed St. Martin, and for a while St. Martin believed he needed Beaumont. It is difficult to imagine that their relationship in the 1820s-30s could have been an equal one, but perhaps it could have been built on greater respect. A respect that today remains the essential keystone of the research relationship.

REFERENCES

1. Weijer C, Emmanuel EJ. Protecting communities in biomedical research. *Science* 2000; 289: 1142-4.
2. Myers JS. *Life and Letters of Dr. William Beaumont.* CV Mosby, St. Louis, 1912.
3. Lovell J [William Beaumont]. A Case of Wounded Stomach. *Medical Recorder* 1825; 8: 19.
4. Beaumont W. *Experiments and Observations on the Gastric Juice, and the Physiology of Digestion.* F. P. Allen, Plattsburgh, 1833.
5. Flexner JT. *Doctors on Horseback: Pioneers of American Medicine.* Windmill Press, Surrey, 1938.
6. Numbers RL. William Beaumont and the Ethics of Human Experimentation. *Journal of the History of Biology* 1979; 12: 113-35.
7. Gaw A. Taylor and the Nazis. In: *Trial By Fire – Lessons from the History of Clinical Trials.* SA Press, Glasgow, 2009.
8. NHS National Patient Safety Agency National Research Ethics Service. Information Sheets & Consent Forms Guidance for Researchers & Reviewers. Version 3.5 May 2009. http://www.nres.npsa.nhs.uk/applications/ guidance/consent-guidance-and-forms/?esctl1417026_ entryid62=67013 [Accessed: 01 July, 2010].
9. ICH-GCP E6 (Section 4.8.10) http://www.ema.europa.eu/pdfs/human/ich/013595en.pdf [Accessed: 01 July, 2010].
10. Tolmie E, Mungall MMB, Louden G, Lindsay GM, Gaw A. Understanding why older people participate in clinical trials: the experience of the Scottish PROSPER participants. *Age and Ageing* 2004; 33: 374-8.
11. Dickert N, Grady C. What's the price of a research subject? Approaches to payment for research participation. *New England Journal of Medicine* 1999; 341: 198-203.
12. Council for International Organizations of Medical Sciences. *International Guidelines for Ethical Review of Epidemiological*

Studies. Guideline 7. World Health Organization, Geneva, 2005.

13. Halpern SD, Karlawish JH, Casarett D, Berlin JA, Asch DA. Empirical assessment of whether moderate payments are undue or unjust inducements for participation in clinical trials. *Archives of Internal Medicine* 2004; 164: 801-3.

14. Bentley JP, Thacker PG. The influence of risk and monetary payment on the research participation decision making process. *Journal of Medical Ethics* 2004; 30: 293-8.

15. Denny C, Grady C. Clinical Research with economically disadvantaged populations *Journal of Medical Ethics* 2007; 33: 382-5.

16. Elliot C. Guinea-pigging: healthy human subjects for drug-safety trials are in demand. But is it a living? *New Yorker* Jan 7, 2008.

4

"The undersigned understands"

Walter Reed and informed consent

The foundation stone of clinical research ethics is that of consent – consent that is given by legally and mentally competent individuals, and that is informed, comprehending and free. The history of clinical research ethics is then largely the history of informed consent. From something of an alien concept, this has evolved, over the last century, into the *sine qua non* of modern research. This history is, however, complex, with long periods of indifference, confusion and disagreement, punctuated by major events in the form of government edicts or reports, often produced in response to scandals recently unearthed by the media.

But, along the way there have been other, less dramatic and much quieter advances which may have helped drive us in the right direction. Sometimes, these have been the adoption by individual investigators of ethical practices that have been novel and ahead of their time. Often, it must be admitted, so ahead of their time that they have failed to make any tangible impact on the slow, yet steady, advance of medical ethics.

One such example is the introduction of written, informed consent forms at the turn of the 20th century – almost 50 years before such an approach was promoted, and almost 80 years before it was mandatory. The investigator at the centre of this story was Walter Reed, a Major in the US Army, who was investigating the causes of yellow fever in 1900.

BACKGROUND

Yellow fever is an acute viral haemorrhagic disease. Its classical presentation is an acute illness with fever, muscle pain, headache, nausea and vomiting. Renal function may be compromised resulting in albuminuria, and liver failure may cause patients to become jaundiced. Estimates of mortality range between 20 - 50%. (1) Thought to have originated in Africa, it travelled to South America along with its mosquito vector, *Aedes aegypti*, most likely on slave ships. (2)

The first recorded outbreak of yellow fever was in Yucatán, Mexico in 1648. With no cure and only a poor understanding of its aetiology and transmission this disease was greatly feared for the next 250 years. (3) Seasonal epidemics, over the course of the 18th and 19th centuries, claimed many thousands of lives. (2) One such epidemic paralysed Philadelphia, the temporary US capital, in 1793, where as many as 5,000 people are believed to have perished. This experience stimulated a medical debate on the nature of yellow fever that would continue into the next century. Many believed that yellow fever emerged from poor environmental conditions, whilst others saw the disease as being imported (e.g. on ships arriving from the Caribbean). A consensus was never reached; however the need for improved sanitary measures and the quarantine of ships potentially carrying the disease were universally accepted.

CUBA

In 1898, US President McKinley declared war on Spain following the sinking of the American battleship *Maine* in Havana harbour. He knew that success in Cuba would not be determined by victory over the Spanish alone, but that his men would also have to survive yellow fever. Since the beginning of conflicts in Cuba in 1895, 16,000 Spanish soldiers had died and many more were disabled as a result of yellow fever. (2)

In previous decades, scientists and physicians had tried desperately to discover more about yellow fever. Germ theory, which was postulated and then confirmed in the late 19th century, led many to believe that the secrets of yellow fever lay beneath the microscope. However, despite the best efforts of scientists, and some erroneous claims of its discovery, the "germ" responsible for yellow fever remained elusive.

Others debated how the disease was transmitted between men. Many believed that yellow fever was maintained in the environment by fomites (clothes, sheets and other objects directly in contact with the sick), however one man suggested an alternative.

Carlos Finlay, a Cuban doctor of Franco-Scottish descent, proposed that the disease was carried by the *Culex* mosquito (now known as *Aedes aegypti*). At the 1881 International Sanitary Conference in Washington, DC, Finlay proposed:

> *the presence of an agent whose existence is entirely independent of the disease and the diseased, but necessary to transmit the disease from an individual afflicted by yellow fever to a healthy person.* (4)

He concluded that in order for yellow fever to be stopped, this agent must be eradicated. Others had demonstrated that disease can be propagated by mosquitoes (5), but Finlay's ideas lay outside mainstream opinion on yellow fever and without incontestable proof, he became the subject of ridicule. (6) However, following the discovery that malaria was transmitted by the *Anopheles* mosquito in 1898, Finlay's theory excited new interest.

In less than one year, the Americans successfully defeated the Spanish and gained control of Cuba. They began a period of occupation whereby they could train Cubans to govern themselves, but were concerned at the losses they were sustaining as a result of disease. Believing the squalid environment to be the cause of disease, American-appointed military governors oversaw a widespread clean-up operation across Cuba. However, whilst improved sanitation reduced cases of dysentery and typhoid, yellow fever remained a danger.

BACILLUS ICTEROIDES

Guiseppe Sanarelli was an Italian scientist working in Montevideo, Uruguay. Like many others, he believed that some, as yet unidentified, bacterium was responsible for yellow fever. In 1897, he claimed its discovery - naming it *Bacillus icteroides*. (7) Having cultured *Bacillus icteroides* from samples taken from the bodies of yellow fever victims, he allegedly infected a number of domestic animals and produced the illness in them. Furthermore, Sanarelli infected five human subjects with *Bacillus icteroides*. As yellow fever is, in fact, a viral disease, it is not possible that he may have induced yellow fever in these subjects, but he certainly caused a severe acute infection that proved fatal in three out of the five cases. The fact that he had failed to seek the consent of his subjects caused outrage amongst his contemporaries. Sir William Osler said of the experiments:

> *To deliberately inject poison of known high virulency into a human being, unless you obtain that man's sanction, is not ridiculous, it is criminal.* (8)

THE YELLOW FEVER BOARD

Many questions remained unanswered and, exasperated and concerned with the situation in Cuba, the US Surgeon-General, George M. Sternberg, recommended a board of physicians be established "for the purpose of pursuing scientific investigations with reference to the infectious disease prevalent on the island of Cuba and especially of yellow fever." (9) He further directed the board to "give special attention to questions relating to the etiology and prevention of yellow fever." (9) His choice to lead the Yellow Fever Board was Maj. Walter Reed, a US Army doctor born in 1851, who had been a prodigy, graduating from medical school at the age of 17 and joining the Army Medical Corps at 23 (fig. 1). Reed would be accompanied by his team - Drs James Carroll, Aristides Agramonte and Jesse Lazear.

A thorough investigation of the aetiology of yellow fever required an evaluation of current thinking. Firstly, they would test Sanarelli's theory implicating *Bacillus icteroides* in the pathogenesis of yellow fever. In July 1900, they cultured blood from eighteen yellow fever patients and later cultured specimens

Figure 1. Studio portrait of Major Walter Reed (1851-1902). (Courtesy of the National Library of Medicine IHM.)

from the autopsies of eleven yellow fever victims. None were positive for Sanarelli's bacillus. (10,11)

With Sanarelli's theory discredited, they met with Carlos Finlay to discuss the possibility that the disease could be transmitted by mosquitoes. Moreover, information from Henry Rose Carter, the chief quarantine officer in Cuba, further supported Finlay's theories. By observing the patterns of infection in his epidemiological studies he suggested that there must be a period of "extrinsic incubation" whereby the disease is rendered capable of infecting another after it leaves an infected patient. This explained why Finlay's own attempts to verify his theory were unsuccessful and gave the Board added momentum.

They began planning their experiments but, from their experience, Reed and his colleagues knew that yellow fever could not be produced in animal models. They needed human volunteers. Perhaps because of the fall-out from the Sanarelli case, Sternberg was acutely aware that the human experiments being planned in Cuba must be conducted to a far higher ethical standard. In May 1900, he wrote directly to Agramonte, the Cuban doctor working with Reed to emphasise the need for such an approach: "you will bear in mind the fact that [the experiments] should not be made on any individual without his full knowledge and consent." (3) Agramonte who was later active in the consent process, especially with the Spanish speaking volunteers, confirmed some years later, "the matter of the experiment was put to them" and that "A written consent was obtained from each one..." (12) Showing great ethical consideration the Board agreed that while they needed to experiment on willing subjects, the "best justification we could offer for experimentation upon others, [was] to submit to the same risk of inoculation ourselves" (Quoted in ref 2).

In August 1900, Reed had to return to Washington, DC to complete other work, but the work of the Board continued in his absence. Lazear and Carroll began work with mosquitoes. At Las Animas Hospital, they "loaded" the mosquitoes with yellow fever, i.e. allowed the mosquitoes to feed on yellow fever patients. For two weeks the mosquitoes then fed on the pair of doctors, but Carroll and Lazear initially remained well. Finally, Carroll developed a severe yellow fever infection. Lazear confirmed the finding by successfully infecting a volunteer and immediately notified Reed of their success.

Having been informed of his colleagues' results, it is likely that Reed ordered all further experiments to be postponed until his return. However, before Reed could return to Cuba, Dr Jesse Lazear contracted yellow fever. Speculation as to whether this was by accident, or deliberate infection continues to this day but, on 25 September 1900, he died aged 34.

On his return, Reed was certain that mosquitoes were responsible for the transmission of yellow fever. He needed, however, to convince a much larger audience. Reed presented his plans for further experiments to General Wood, and made it clear that more human subjects would be required. He saw the young and immunologically naïve Spanish immigrant population as a suitable study group and asked General Wood to approach the Spanish Consul for approval on his behalf. With an appreciation of the importance of Reed's work, Wood offered his full support and US $10,000 to aid the project.

In November 1900, Camp Lazear (named in memory of their colleague) was opened and experiments began. Participants were recruited from the US Army or from the Spanish immigration station in Havana. Agramonte, a native Spanish speaker, would go daily to the immigration station where he would hire around ten men to come and work on the camp gathering stones. The men were very well looked after and during their stay a detailed medical history was taken to identify those who may have previously encountered the disease. Agramonte also ensured that the men were at least 24 years old, the age of legal maturity in Cuba at the time.

After a discussion of the experiments with those who were eligible, written consent was obtained, and details of how they would be compensated for their participation were given. The original signed consent form of one of the Spanish volunteers, Antonio Benigno is shown in fig. 2, and its English transcript is shown in fig. 3. US soldiers and civilians also volunteered to be part of the experiments. Two were Private John R. Kissinger and civilian clerk John J. Moran. They refused payment declaring that their co-operation relied "solely in the interest of humanity and the cause of science." (13)

By February 1901, 18 Americans and 15 Spanish immigrants had participated in studies at Camp Lazear. (3) These had involved exposing human subjects to fomites from yellow fever victims, subcutaneous injection of blood from yellow fever sufferers, and exposure to mosquitoes "loaded" by exposure to yellow fever patients.

Reed and his colleagues presented their findings at the Pan-American Medical congress and published their results to acclaim. (9, 11) They had successfully ruled out fomites as a means of transmission and concluded that the *Aedes aegypti* mosquito was responsible for the propagation of yellow fever and that its destruction, in conjunction with steps taken to protect individuals from being bitten, could effectively control yellow fever. (11)

Despite the causative agent remaining elusive, Maj. William Gorgas, the chief sanitation officer in Havana, could begin the task of destroying the mosquito. In just a few short months, these measures delivered extraordinary success.

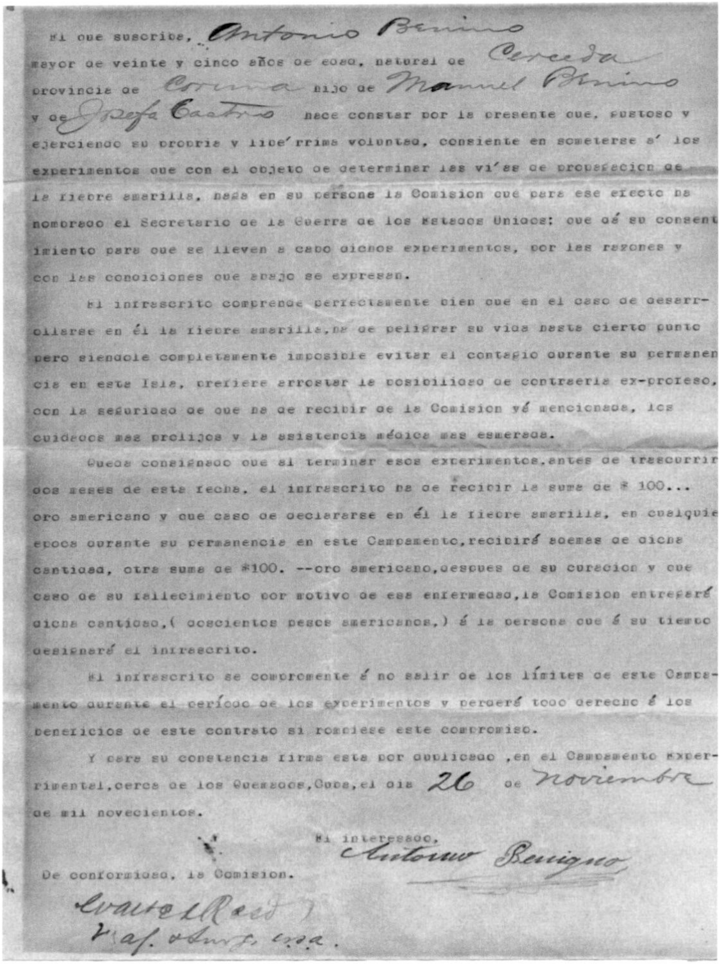

El que suscribe, Antonio Benino mayor de veinte y cinco años de edad, natural de Cerceda provincia de Coruña hijo de Manuel Benino y de Josefa Castro hace constar por la presente que, gustoso y ejerciendo su propia y libre'rrima voluntad, consiente en someterse á los experimentos que con el objeto de determinar las ví'as de propagación de la fiebre amarilla, haga en su persona la Comisión que para ese efecto ha nombrado el Secretario de la Guerra de los Estados Unidos; que dá su consentimiento para que se lleven á cabo dichos experimentos, por las razones y con las condiciones que abajo se expresan.

El infrascrito comprende perfectamente bien que en el caso de desarrollarse en él la fiebre amarilla, ha de peligrar su vida hasta cierto punto pero siendole completamente imposible evitar el contagio durante su permanencia en esta Isla, prefiere arrostar la posibilidad de contraerla ex-profeso, con la seguridad de que ha de recibir de la Comisión yá mencionada, los cuidados mas prolijos y la asistencia médica mas esmerada.

Queda consignado que al terminar esos experimentos, antes de trascurrir dos meses de esta fecha, el infrascrito ha de recibir la suma de $ 100... oro americano y que caso de declararse en él la fiebre amarilla, en cualquier época durante su permanencia en este Campamento, recibirá ademas de dicha cantidad, otra suma de $100. --oro americano, despues de su curación y que caso de su fallecimiento por motivo de esa enfermedad, la Comisión entregará dicha cantidad, (doscientos pesos americanos,) á la persona que á su tiempo designará el infrascrito.

El infrascrito se compromete á no salir de los límites de este Campamento durante el período de los experimentos y perderá todo derecho á los beneficios de este contrato si rompiese este compromiso.

Y para su constancia firma esta por duplicado, en el Campamento Experimental, cerca de los Quemados, Cuba, el dia 26 de noviembre de mil novecientos.

El interesado,
Antonio Benigno

De conformidad, la Comisión.

Walter Reed
Maj. & Surg., U.S.A.

Figure 2. The original Spanish contract between Walter Reed and one of the Camp Lazear volunteers, Antonio Benigno/Benino, with signatures of both parties. (Reproduced with permission. Courtesy of Historical Collections & Services, Claude Moore Health Sciences Library, University of Virginia.)

The undersigned, Antonio Benino being more than twenty-five years of age, native of Cerceda, in the province of Corima, the son of Manuel Benino and Josefa Castro here states by these presents, being in the enjoyment and exercise of his own very free will, that he consents to submit himself to experiments for the purpose of determining the methods of transmission of yellow fever, made upon his person by the Commission appointed for this purpose by the Secretary of War of the United States, and that he gives his consent to undergo the said experiments for the reasons and under the conditions below stated.

The undersigned understands perfectly well that in case of the development of yellow fever in him, that he endangers his life to a certain extent but it being entirely impossible for him to avoid the infection during his stay in this island, he prefers to take the chance of contracting it intentionally in the belief that he will receive from the said Commission the greatest care and the most skillful medical service.

It is understood that at the completion of these experiments, within two months from this date, the undersigned will receive the sum of $100 in American gold and that in case of his contracting yellow fever at any time during his residence in this camp, he will receive in addition to that sum a further sum of $100 in American gold, upon his recovery and that in case of his death because of this disease, the Commission will transmit the said sum (two hundred American dollars) to the person whom the undersigned shall designate at his convenience.

The undersigned binds himself not to leave the bounds of this camp during the period of the experiments and will forfeit all right to the benefits named in this contract if he breaks this agreement.

And to bind himself he signs this paper in duplicate, in the Experimental Camp, near Quemados, Cuba, on the 26th day of November nineteen hundred.

The contracting party,
Antonio Benigno
On the part of the Commission:

Walter Reed
Maj. & Surg., U.S.A.

Figure 3. English transcript of the original Spanish contract between Walter Reed and Antonio Benigno/Benino. (Reproduced with permission. Courtesy of Historical Collections & Services, Claude Moore Health Sciences Library, University of Virginia.)

Reed was hailed as a medical hero in the US, but died prematurely in 1902, not from yellow fever like his colleague Lazear, but from complications following a simple appendicectomy.

DEVELOPMENT OF INFORMED CONSENT

Although the notion of consent had been well recognized for several hundred years, the concept of "informed consent" was first mooted in 1947, when the General Manager of the newly created US Atomic Energy Commission, Carroll Wilson, laid down rules for human research. These specified that the "patient give his complete and informed consent in writing."(14) This is believed to be the first conjunction of the terms "informed" and "consent".

In the same year, this concept of informed consent was developed and strengthened by the judges at the Nuremberg Doctors' Trial. They stated, in the preamble to their sentencing, the ten principles that should guide ethical biomedical research. These have subsequently become known as the Nuremberg Code. (15) (See appendix 1) The first of these principles, and the basis for all the others, is the express need for consent – "The voluntary consent of the human subject is absolutely essential." This principle goes on to demand that the subject be legally competent, should be free to make a choice, and should be sufficiently informed "to make an understanding and enlightened decision."

Throughout the next two and a half decades, the nature, importance and practicability of informed consent was much debated, and the implementation of the principles set forth in the Nuremberg Code were variably applied.

Even stalwarts of medical ethics such as Henry Knowles Beecher, whose work in the 1960s exposed many abuses of research ethics, felt the Code to be fundamentally flawed (16), and not necessarily applicable in practice. In 1964, the World Medical Association adopted and disseminated to its membership a set of guidelines for human experimentation, now known as the Declaration of Helsinki.

This document is a major landmark, but even it, in its original version, was equivocal about the absolute need for informed consent, allowing physicians to decide whether consent was "consistent with patient psychology" in some trials. (16) Importantly, however, this document did introduce the concept of consent by proxy for the first time – a notable, and often criticized, omission from the Nuremberg Code. (16) This is an essential component of taking consent when the prospective research participant is a minor or an incapacitated adult.

A decade later, in 1974, the National Commission for the Protection of Human Subjects of Biomedical and Behavioral Research was established in the US, largely as a consequence of the exposé of Tuskegee Study. (17) Over the next four years this Commission produced 17 reports and appendices, the most notable of which was the Belmont Report in 1978. (18) The Commission established three basic principles on which the ethical conduct of clinical research should be built: *respect for persons*, *beneficence* and *justice*. Furthermore in their detailed analysis of informed consent they defined that such consent required three necessary conditions: *information*, *comprehension* and *voluntariness*.

TESTING REED'S APPROACH

At first glance, Reed's approach would appear to satisfy the three conditions of informed consent from the Belmont Report: the "contract" gives *information* with no holds barred – "The undersigned understands perfectly well that in case of the development of yellow fever in him, that he endangers his life…" is supplemented with discussion to ensure *comprehension* and, as far as can be discerned appears to have been *voluntary*. Certainly the documented drop-out of one subject just before the sub-cutaneous injection experiment commenced implies that there was no overwhelming compulsion to take part. (2)

If we further challenge Reed's consent process against a modern and even more stringent practical test – viz. the components of informed consent as laid down in the ICH-GCP guidelines (19), we find that, of the 20 points to be covered, his approach satisfies at least 8 or 9 of them. A further 3 points are largely irrelevant to the yellow fever studies, leaving approximately 8 that are unsatisfied. These relate, for example, to inclusion of details of the experimental procedures, the number of trial subjects, and the right to withdraw. As noted above there was a discussion with prospective participants prior to their enrollment in either English or Spanish as appropriate, but we do not have details of the topics covered. Some, or all, of the points not covered in the information sheet/consent form may have been discussed with the men. Overall, Reed's "contracts" do remarkably well when judged by 21st century standards, especially as he had no professional guidelines to follow other than his Hippocratic Oath.

WRITTEN CONSENT

One very important aspect of Reed's approach was to obtain consent in writing from his study participants. Many regard the taking of consent as akin to the forging of a contract between researcher and participant. As such it is not surprising that the use of legalized forms that must be signed and dated by both parties has become the norm. Indeed, the ICH–GCP guidelines (section 8.3.12) state that signed informed consent forms are required "To document that consent is obtained in accordance with GCP and protocol and dated prior to participation of each subject in trial." (19)   Similarly, the UK legislation pertaining to Clinical Trials of Investigational Medicinal Products states that informed consent must be "evidenced in writing." (20)

However, we must be aware that obtaining consent is not an event, but a process. As CIOMS notes, "Obtaining informed consent is a process that is begun when initial contact is made with a prospective subject and continues throughout the course of the study." (21) Thus, the signing of the consent form is only one aspect of this process, but nonetheless an important one. Consent forms should therefore be regarded, not as legal contractual documents, but rather written records of the dialogue that has taken place between researcher and participant, supplemented and supported with written materials, usually in the form of a patient information sheet. It is this dialogue that makes the consent truly informed.

CONCLUSIONS

Reed and his colleagues were considerably ahead of their time in requiring their research participants to sign an almost modern style consent form. Moreover, this was done after discussion of the subjects in their own language, whether English or Spanish, and their consent appears to have been respectfully elicited and freely given. It would be gratifying to claim that Reed's approach to consent was a turning point in research ethics, but the simple truth is that it was not. It did not mark a change in research conduct, and now appears as an anomaly in the timeline of research ethics, as we have to wait almost 50 years before we see a similar approach being advocated. That said, if every study in that intervening half century, and many of those in the next, had adopted a consent process similar to Reed's, the history of informed consent and therefore of research ethics would have been very different.

REFERENCES

1. Greenwood D, Slack RCB, Peutherer JF. *Medical Microbiology.* 16th Edition. Churchill Livingstone, Edinburgh, 2002.

2. Pierce JR, Writer J. *Yellow Jack: How Yellow Fever Ravaged America and Walter Reed Discovered Its Deadly Secrets.* John Wiley & Sons, Inc., New Jersey, 2005.

3. Lederer S. Walter Reed and the Yellow Fever Experiments. In: *The Oxford Textbook of Clinical Research Ethics.* Emanuel EJ, Lie RK, Grady C, Miller FG, Crouch RA, Wendler D (Eds). Oxford University Press, Oxford, 2008.

4. Sanchez JL. *Carlos J. Finlay: His life and work.* Editorial José Martí, La Habana, 1999.

5. Chernin E. Patrick Manson (1844-1922) and the transmission of filariasis. *American Journal of Tropical Medicine and Hygiene* 1977; 26; 1065-9.

6. Chaves-Carballo E. Carlos Finlay and yellow fever: triumph over adversity. *Military Medicine* 2005; 170: 881-5.

7. Sanarelli, G. A Lecture on Yellow Fever. With a description of the Bacillus Icteroides: Delivered before the University of Montevideo on June 10th, 1897. *British Medical Journal* 1897; 2: 7–11.

8. Osler W, Vaughan V. The Bacillus icteroides (Sanarelli) and Bacillus X (Sternberg). *Transactions of the Association of American Physicians.* 1898; 13: 61-72.

9. Reed W, Carroll J, Agramonte A, Lazear JW. The Etiology of Yellow Fever—A Preliminary Note. *Public Health Papers and Reports.* 1900; 26: 37–53.

10. Reed W, Carroll J. A comparative study of the biological characters and pathogenesis of Bacillus X (Sternberg), Bacillus icteroides (Sanarelli), and the Hog-Cholera Bacillus (Salmon and Smith). *Journal of Experimental Medicine* 1900; 5: 215–70.

11. Reed W, Carroll J, Agramonte A. The Etiology of Yellow Fever – An Additional Note. *Journal of the American Medical Association*. 1901; XXXVI: 431-40.

12. Agramonte A. The inside story of a great medical discovery. *Scientific Monthly* 1915; 1: 209-37.

13. Owen RL. Senate Document No. 822. *Yellow fever: a compilation of various publications: results of the work of Maj. Walter Reed, Medical Corps, United States Army, and the Yellow Fever Commission*. Washington, DC: Government Printing Office, 1911.

14. Moreno JD, Lederer SE. Revising the history of cold war research ethics. *Kennedy Institute of Ethics Journal* 1996; 6: 223-7.

15. Trials of War Criminals before the Nuremberg Military Tribunals under Control Council Law No. 10. Nuremberg, October 1946–April 1949. Washington, DC: U.S. G.P.O, 1949–1953.

16. Blacksher E, Moreno JD. A history of informed consent in clinical research. In: *The Oxford Textbook of Clinical Research Ethics*. Emanuel EJ, Lie RK, Grady C, Miller FG, Crouch RA, Wendler D (Eds). Oxford University Press, Oxford, 2008.

17. Gaw A. Clinton and the apology. In: *Trial by Fire – Lessons from the History of Clinical Trials*. SA Press, Glasgow, 2009.

18. National Commission for the Protection of Human Subjects of Biomedical and Behavioral Research. *The Belmont Report Ethical Principles and Guidelines for the protection of human subjects of research*. http://ohsr.od.nih.gov/guidelines/belmont.html [Accessed: 28 July, 2010].

19. ICH-GCP E6. http://www.ema.europa.eu/pdfs/human/ich/013595en.pdf [Accessed: 05 July, 2010].

20. The Medicines for Human Use (Clinical Trials) Regulations 2004. http://www.aapec.org.uk/documents/MHRA.pdf [Accessed: 05 July, 2010].

21. Council for International Organizations of Medical Sciences (CIOMS) in collaboration with the World Health Organization (WHO). *International Ethical Guidelines for Biomedical Research Involving Human Subjects.* World Health Organization, Geneva, 2002.

5

"More subtle degrees of contempt"

Leo Alexander and codes of practice

The court had been in session for 139 days; it had heard the testimony of 85 witnesses and received more than 1,400 documents by way of evidence. (1) Now the legal battle was over and the courtroom was hushed in anticipation of the outcome. Twenty-three defendants, all but three of whom were doctors, awaited their fate at the hands of a panel of American judges. The date was August 19th, 1947; the court – the Palace of Justice in Nuremberg in occupied post-war Germany; the trial one of the most famous in legal history – the Nazi Doctors' Trial. (2)

In a judgement running to more than 50,000 words, pronouncing the guilt of 16 of the defendants and sending 7 to their death, a small section of no more than 500 words entitled, "Permissible Medical Experiments" might initially have been overlooked. However, this was to be the enduring legacy of the Nuremberg Doctors' Trial – ten carefully weighed and worded standards that should be applied to those conducting human research, which have since become known as the Nuremberg Code (See appendix 1).

The precise authorship of the code is unknown. Brigadier General Telford Taylor, military lawyer and the Chief Counsel for the Prosecution at the Doctors' Trial, believed it was from the hand of one of the four judges, Harold Sebring. (3) Other commentators have suggested that two physicians were the chief architects of the Code: Drs Andrew C. Ivy and Leo Alexander (fig.1). (3-6) It is the contributions of the latter, and more junior contender, that have come to be thought of as the most important, and it is Alexander's journey to Nuremberg and beyond, that we wish to retrace.

Figure 1. Leo Alexander (1905-85).

BACKGROUND

Leo Alexander was an Austrian Jew from a Viennese intellectual background – his mother wealthy, his father an eminent professor of ear, nose and throat surgery, and his home a salon for the likes of Freud and Mahler. (4) He idolised his father and cited him as a key motivating factor in his ultimate career choice, training as a doctor in Germany.

Alexander was hard working and fiercely ambitious, perhaps in an attempt to emulate and surpass the achievements of his father, and soon began to make his own impression on the scientific community. In 1929 he began an internship at a respected institution in Frankfurt where he developed an interest in neuropathology and psychiatry. He remained there for several years until he was invited to Beijing on an eight-month secondment as an honorary professor.

He left Germany in February 1933, confident that he would return, better able to continue his already burgeoning career. However, shortly after his departure, the Nazis took power in Germany and Alexander would not return for the next twelve years. Shocked and disheartened, the exiled Alexander struggled to decide on his next move. Like many other European Jews he eventually managed to travel to the US where he was able to continue his work in neurology and psychiatry. He married a young American woman and became a US citizen. (4)

Following an initial struggle to integrate himself into American society, Alexander moved to Boston and established himself as part of the scientific community there. With the outbreak of war, Alexander was keen to join the war effort and, in 1942, he enlisted in the US Army Medical Corps. He was then transferred to England in October 1943, where he remained until the end of the war, providing medical support for the American Eighth Air Force Base. (3)

WAR CRIMES

With the war won, a new battle was raging for the Allies – to capture and hold to account those guilty of committing war crimes. In May 1945, Alexander was given orders to make a "complete survey of the neuropsychiatric work of the German army and *Luftwaffe*, as well as civilian agencies." (4) It was in this role that he would scrutinise the practices of the very scientists and institutions, which, 12 years previously, he had seen as his colleagues and competition.

Why Alexander was chosen for the task remains uncertain, although he was certainly ideally suited. He was a doctor, a native German speaker and fully versed in the pre-war German medical system, and indeed familiar with many of the principal physicians. He was also highly motivated to seek justice for the way the Nazis had affected his country, his family and his career. However, Alexander commented light-heartedly that his appointment was made by a young lieutenant in the Air Force who had studied under him at Duke University and who had chosen Alexander from an alphabetical list of qualified persons, because he was near the top. (4)

Alexander spent two arduous months combing the entire country for evidence relating to neuropsychiatric research in Germany during the war before producing eight reports for the Combined Intelligence Objectives Subcommittee. The most significant of these concerned freezing experiments that took place on camp inmates at Dachau. (7) It was with the help of evidence from this report that Justice Robert Jackson, prosecutor at the International Military Tribunal highlighted to the wider world the extent of the atrocities committed by the Nazi regime.

Thus, Alexander had established himself as a determined and reliable war crimes investigator and was uniquely placed to be appointed as medical expert to the Nuremberg Doctors' Trial that followed (fig. 2).

THE DOCTORS' TRIAL

In the Doctors' trial, or more formally *The United States vs. Karl Brandt et al* (2), the 23 defendants were indicted on four counts:

1. Conspiracy to commit war crimes and crimes against humanity
2. War crimes (i.e., crimes against persons protected by the laws of war, such as prisoners of war)
3. Crimes against humanity (including persons not protected by the laws of war)
4. Membership of a criminal organisation (the SS).

As the war neared its conclusion, details of the medical experimentation in concentration camps began to reach the world press. The public needed no convincing that the Nazi doctors involved in unethical medical experimentation were guilty of unimaginable cruelty; however, in order for them to face criminal charges, the American prosecutors faced a dilemma.

Ironically, Germany was in fact the only country in the world at that time with legally binding and ethically advanced guidelines on human experimentation. In 1900, following Albert Neisser's unethical attempts to vaccinate healthy individuals against syphilis, the German minister for Religious, Education and Medical Affairs issued a directive, known as the Berlin Code, which required the "unambiguous consent" of the subject after considering a "proper explanation of the possible negative consequences" of the intervention. (8)

Figure 2. Leo Alexander pointing out the scars on the leg of Ravensbrück survivor, Jadwiga Dzido, who appeared as a witness at the Doctors' Trial on 22 December, 1946. (Reproduced with permission. Courtesy of the United States Holocaust Memorial Museum.)

Subjects involved in medical research in Germany received greater protection when, in 1931, the Reichsrundschreiben document entitled "Regulations on New Therapy and Human Experimentation" made informed consent and other minimum standards for ethical practice legally binding. (9) Despite this, the defendants in Nuremberg would claim their innocence, stating that they were acting in accordance with German military law (4), and that their American medical counterparts were involved in similar practices.

It was clearly of the utmost importance to distinguish the practices of the physicians in the dock from those of Allied researchers. With this objective in mind, Leo Alexander, as medical advisor for the prosecution, was determined to unravel what had motivated these doctors to ignore their Hippocratic Oath and to commit such harm. He was convinced that Nazi doctors had not conducted experiments under orders from the state to benefit the German army, as some defendants argued, but rather that they were "frankly and openly devoted to methods of destroying or preventing life." (4) He argued that:

> *the experiments were amateurish and poorly coordinated, that they failed to give the scientific information which was claimed to be desired, and that a unified policy was completely absent, except for the barbaric manner of their execution.* (4)

In November 1946, Alexander coined the term *thanatology*, the science of killing, and argued that German medical research amounted to the development of the scientific technique of genocide. Thus, despite concerns over the misconduct of American researchers with regard to experimentation on prisoners and asylum inmates, the development of this concept allowed the practices of Allied and Nazi physicians to be wholly differentiated, at least at the level of motivation.

The prosecution also had to determine what they believed to be ethically permissible human experimentation and what was not. This was necessary for successfully holding the defendants to account but, much more importantly, to ensure that no such experiments could ever take place again.

THE GENESIS OF THE CODE

In April 1947, Leo Alexander sent a memo to Telford Taylor outlining six points covering ethical conduct of clinical research. (4) In summary, these were:

1. The requirement for legally valid and freely given informed consent by the subject or their proxy
2. The need for experiments to be humanitarian in nature
3. That the results of the proposed study should not be already known or likely to result in harm to the subject
4. The need for appropriately skilled staff and suitable facilities
5. That risks should not outweigh the benefits of the study
6. That studies should be built on sound scientific grounds and on a foundation of previous preclinical data.

Although there is some doubt about the precise date of this document many of the words used by Alexander in defining his six standards did find their way into the Code as stated in the final judgement four months later.

The eminent physiologist and physician Andrew C. Ivy, who was the American Medical Association's representative at the trial, also outlined his approach to research ethics, discussing these during four days of testimony as a witness at the trial (fig. 3). (3) In summary, Ivy's points were:

1. the need for free and informed consent
2. the scientifically robust design of research studies based on preclinical work
3. the need for studies to be conducted by scientifically qualified staff.

There is obvious overlap between Alexander's approach and that of Ivy. How much the two men conferred is unknown, but it is hard to imagine that two US physicians would not have shared some of their thoughts even in informal discussion. Whatever the case, both are generally credited with laying the groundwork for the judges' exposition of the Code.

Figure 3. Andrew C. Ivy (1893-1978) being sworn in at the Doctors' Trial in Nuremberg.

The full Code can be viewed in Appendix 1. Three main themes are evident. First that the absolute need for informed consent is presented as a *sine qua non* of clinical research; second that a study participant's rights are given precedence over those of the investigator; and third that the investigator has clear obligations regarding the design and conduct of the study.

One of the major concerns raised by the Code was the rigidity attached to the need for informed consent from the subjects themselves. (10) This would appear to immediately preclude the recruitment of any individual unable, through legal or medical incompetence, of giving their own consent. Studies in minors and in incapacitated adults would not be possible as consent by proxies would be required in these cases. Alexander addressed this issue in his memo, which called for the acknowledgement of consent by proxy in certain settings. However, this recommendation, at least, was ignored by the judges.

HOW WAS THE NUREMBERG CODE RECEIVED?

A code such as that from Nuremberg is a recommended ethical framework within which professionals should work. Although pronounced in a court of law it is not, in itself, a law. Many conflate legality with morality, confusing such codes of ethics with legally binding statutes. Simply designating an action as unethical does not make it illegal. Similarly, the illegality of an action does not immediately make it immoral. This has importance when we come to consider the problems of implementing codes of practice. Without the weight of the law behind them they become nothing more than voluntary guidelines, which we may choose to follow or not. In the case of the Nuremberg Code, it was largely ignored by the medical profession, especially in the US and the UK, for twenty years after its publication. (11) It was however, used as the framework to draft legal instruments in a number of countries and even individual states such as California. (12)

The voluntary nature of a code of ethics may be viewed as its principal strength in that the best possible, and most liberated, scientific environments are created not within the straightjackets of legislation, but within the relative flexibility afforded by a professional guideline. Unfortunately, against this contention is the evidence of history. Time and again we have learned that we cannot rely on "the presence of an intelligent, informed, conscientious, compassionate, responsible investigator" (13) guided merely by a voluntary code of conduct. For the safety of trial participants that investigator must also be constrained by the rule of law.

The relevance of the Nuremberg Code to those outside the courtroom and conducting medical research throughout the world was widely debated. There were some who felt that, as America's response to Nazi doctors, it had little to offer non-Nazi physicians – including all those who practiced in accordance with the Hippocratic tradition. In fact, this could be said of Leo Alexander himself, who, in a letter to the *New England Journal of Medicine* in 1973, argued against a state law designed to protect psychiatric patients by limiting the number of electroconvulsive treatments they could receive in one year. In his opinion, if a physician felt it necessary for the good of his patients to prescribe more treatments then he should do so:

> ...*such temporal laws, in comparison to our Hippocratic obligation, enduring throughout the entire history of medicine are merely words written into sand.* (14)

However, earlier in his career, just two years after Nuremberg, Alexander had cautioned his American colleagues to heed the lessons learned and to acknowledge that history may repeat itself. Alexander stated:

> *Whatever proportions these crimes finally assumed, it became evident to all who investigated them that they had started from small*

beginnings. The beginnings at first were merely a subtle shift in emphasis in the basis attitude of the physicians. It started with the acceptance of the attitude…that there is such a thing as a life not worthy to be lived. (15)

Perhaps sensitized by his experiences in Nuremberg, Alexander was keen to warn others of the slippery slope of research ethics – a slope that could just as easily be found in the US as in Nazi Germany.

THE LEGACY OF THE CODE

The Nuremberg code has probably shaped every subsequent ethical code of conduct regarding human experimentation. (10) One of the most influential and widely adopted of these was the Declaration of Helsinki from the World Medical Association (WMA) (See appendix 2).

The WMA, a global association of physicians, was founded in 1947 in order to address concerns over the Nazi medical atrocities. It has a remit to establish and maintain the highest ethical standards for doctors. In response to the judgements at Nuremberg and the publication of the Nuremberg Code, the WMA embarked on a 17-year journey towards the Declaration of Helsinki. This document was adopted in 1964, after first being drafted in 1961, and was built upon a series of preceding statements, resolutions and declarations including the 1954 Resolution on Human Experimentation. (16) The latter clearly set out the requirement for researchers to inform their subjects fully and allowed for proxy consent in incapacitated or incompetent individuals.

The 1964 Declaration of Helsinki further softened the absolute requirement for consent by the subject that was central to the Nuremberg Code when it stated: "If at all possible, consistent with patient psychology, the doctor should obtain the patient's freely given consent..." (17)   Such a conditional statement appears to leave much to the discretion of the individual investigator and was considered a troubling departure from the rigid standards set out in Nuremberg.

The Declaration of Helsinki is, however, very much a living document and it has been subject to revision and review several times over the years. In 1975, it was revised in Tokyo where the need for informed consent was repositioned front and centre, and it required any physician wishing to avoid obtaining consent to justify this to an independent ethics committee. (17)

More recently, adherence to the principles of the Declaration of Helsinki have been enshrined as one of the principles of Good Clinical Practice, which is now part of the legal framework for the conduct of clinical trials in humans involving investigational medicinal products in Europe (See appendix 3).

THE HISTORICAL RELEVANCE OF THE CODE

The Nuremberg Code has been described by many as the most important document ever written on human research ethics. While it undoubtedly has a central place in the development of modern research ethics, such a superlative may be questioned. As noted above, the Code was largely ignored for around two decades. This may have been due to the circumstances that prompted the Code – a series of medical atrocities conducted by Nazis during a war – that were seen as irrelevant and unconnected with medical practices in other countries. However, in the mid 1960's a number of important events occurred that refocused professional and public attention on the issues. These were the publication of the Declaration of Helsinki in 1964 (16,17); an important review article by the American anaesthetist, Henry K. Beecher, in the *New England*

Journal of Medicine in 1966 (13); and the book, *Human Guinea Pigs*, by the English physician, Maurice H. Pappworth, in 1967 (18). The latter two publications contained catalogues of unethical human research performed in the post war period and compiled by the respective authors. Collectively, these three events pushed forward the need for change and tighter control of medical research.

The rapidly changing social and cultural backdrop of the 1960s may also have significantly contributed to this development. Every idea has its time, and in the late 1940s the medical profession was not ready to address the ethical issues central to the Code. By the 1960s, it was.

But what would the research ethics landscape look like today if there had been no Nuremberg Code? While this counterfactual may be regarded as a meaningless exercise, it does allow us to consider the true historical importance of the Code. As the document was largely ignored after its publication it is difficult to claim that it prevented many unethical experiments from being conducted in what remained of the 1940s and the 1950s, as demonstrated by Beecher and Pappworth. Indeed, the scale of the unethical practices they exposed would lend support to the notion that the Code had no impact at all. Without the Code, however, these whistle-blowers would have had no moral yardstick by which to judge these misdemeanors. The Nuremberg Code, like all codes of practice, set a standard. Whether that standard is followed is another matter, but its very existence provides a profession, and the observers of that profession, with the means to distinguish right from wrong.

Such a code, however, already existed for the medical profession in the form of the Hippocratic Oath. What did the Nuremberg Code add to this, if anything? Both, place our patients at the centre of our work, along with an over-riding requirement for beneficence and non-maleficence. Neither the Code nor the

Oath has the force of law behind it and both rely upon voluntary professional adoption to be meaningful.

The Nuremberg Code, however, is primarily concerned with research rather than practice, and emphasizes the importance and need for informed consent in that setting. This importance may be implicit in the Hippocratic tradition, but only the Code insists that it is the foundation stone of all human research. The concept of informed consent had been a major concern of researchers as early as 1900 (see chapter 4), but the Nuremberg Code was the first international formulation of it.

Had the Nuremberg Code been in existence before the Second World War would the atrocities that took place in camps such as Dachau and Ravensbrück have happened? Leo Alexander, himself, recognized that such a Code would have prevented nothing and its existence would not stop other totalitarian regimes similarly bent on a path of medical experimentation, when he said:

> *It is evident, of course, that the crimes to which this code owes its formulation could not have occurred in any country in which the ordinary laws concerning murder, manslaughter, mayhem, assault, and battery had not been suspended in regard to all or certain groups of its citizens and inhabitants. This Code is also unlikely to prevent another dictatorial government from repeating the crimes of the National Socialist Government.* (19)

However, he points out that the Code, in which he played such a central authorship role, may serve to protect particularly vulnerable individuals in otherwise humane societies:

> *Nevertheless, it is a useful measure by which to prevent in less blatant settings the consequences of more subtle degrees of contempt for the rights and dignity of certain classes of human beings, such as mental defectives, people presumably dying from incurable illnesses, and people otherwise disenfranchised, such as prisoners or other*

inarticulate public charges whose rights might be easily disregarded for the apparently compelling reason of an urgent purpose. (19)

CONCLUSIONS

Alexander's legacy was an important one. As one of the principal authors of the Nuremberg Code he set in train a movement that has slowly, but inexorably, led us to the present day matrix of research ethical codes in which we work. It seems unthinkable today that the medical atrocities perpetrated in the Nazi concentrations camps could happen again, but what Alexander and his colleagues still ask us to do is to think exactly that. Having robust codes of ethics coupled with legally binding regulations derived from the Nuremberg Code helps to ensure that the past does not happen again.

REFERENCES

1.   Trials of War Criminals before the Nuernberg Military Tribunals under Control Council Law No. 10. Volume II. US Government Printing Office, Washington, DC. 1949. Available at http://www.loc.gov/rr/frd/Military_Law/pdf/NT_war-criminals_Vol-II.pdf [Accessed: 23 November, 2010]
2.   United States v Karl Brandt et al. Trials Of War Criminals. Washington, DC: Government Printing Office, 1949.
3.   Shuster E. Fifty years later: the significance of the Nuremberg Code. *New England Journal of Medicine*. 1997; 13: 1436-40.
4.   Schmidt U. *Justice at Nuremberg. Leo Alexander and the Nazi Doctors' Trial.* Palgrave Macmillan, Basingstoke, 2006.
5.   Grodin MA. Historical origins of the Nuremberg Code. In: *The Nazi Doctors and the Nuremberg Code: Human Rights in Human Experimentation.* Annas GJ and Grodin MA (Eds). Oxford University Press, Oxford, 1992.

6.   Temme LA. Ethics in human experimentation: the two military physicians who helped develop the Nuremberg Code. *Aviation Space and Environmental Medicine* 2003; 74: 1297–1300.

7.   Alexander L. *The treatment of shock from prolonged exposure to cold, especially in water. Combined Intelligence Objectives Subcommittee. Target No.24. Report No. 250.* Washington, DC: Office of Publication Board, Department of Commerce, 1946.

8.   Vollmann, J, Winau R. Informed consent in human experimentation before the Nuremberg code. *British Medical Journal* 1996; 313: 1445-7.

9.   Sass HM. Reichsrundschreiben 1931: Pre-Nuremberg German regulations concerning new therapy and human experimentation. *Journal of Medical Philosophy* 1983; 8: 99-111.

10. Annas GJ and Grodin MA. The Nuremberg Code. In: *The Oxford Textbook of Clinical Research Ethics.* Emanuel EJ, Lie RK, Grady C, Miller FG, Crouch RA, Wendler D (Eds). Oxford University Press, Oxford, 2008.

11. Doyal L. Introduction to Beecher's "Ethics and clinical research". In: *Informed consent and medical research.* Doyal L and Tobias JS (Eds). BMJ Books, London, 2001.

12. State of California Health and Safety Code Section 24170-24179.5 Available at http://www.leginfo.ca.gov/cgi-bin/displaycode?section=hsc&group=24001-25000&file=24170-24179.5 [Accessed: 29 November 2010].

13. Beecher HK. Ethics and clinical research. *New England Journal of Medicine.* 1966; 274: 1354-60.

14. Alexander L. Temporal Laws and Medical Ethics in Conflict. *New England Journal of Medicine.* 1973; 289: 324-5

15. Alexander L. Medical science under dictatorship. *New England Journal of Medicine.* 1949; 249 39-47.

16. Ashcroft RE. The Declaration of Helsinki. In: *The Oxford Textbook of Clinical Research Ethics.* Emanuel EJ, Lie RK,

Grady C, Miller FG, Crouch RA, Wendler D (Eds). Oxford University Press, Oxford, 2008.

17. Brody B. A historical introduction to the requirement of obtaining informed consent from research participants. In: *Informed consent and medical research.* Doyal L and Tobias JS (Eds). BMJ Books, London, 2001.

18. Pappworth MH. *Human guinea pigs: experimentation on man.* Routledge and Kegan Paul, London, 1967.

19. Alexander L. Limitations of experimentation on human beings with special reference to psychiatric patients. *Diseases of the Nervous System* 1966; 27: 61-5.

6

"Out of troubling practices"
Henry Knowles Beecher
and whistle-blowing

When we discover wrongdoing we have two choices: we can either turn away and ignore the problem, or we can confront it. When that wrongdoing concerns the actions of our professional colleagues, to confront it risks our own professional standing and opens us up to the opprobrium of our peers. To confront it, therefore, takes courage – more courage than most of us could muster – and an over-riding belief that exposing the wrongdoing is in the best interests of the wider community. In the 1960s an American academic anaesthetist from Harvard, named Henry Knowles Beecher (fig.1) put his reputation on the line and risked vilification, when he blew the whistle on what he saw as the unethical clinical research practices of many of his colleagues.

Figure 1. Henry Knowles Beecher (1904-76). (Photograph courtesy of The Hastings Center.)

BACKGROUND

Beecher was born Henry Unangst in Kansas on February 4, 1904, changing his name in his early 20s after the influential 19th century preacher Henry Ward Beecher. He studied chemistry at the University of Kansas and received a BA in 1926 and a MA in 1927. (1) In 1928 he moved to Boston and enrolled in Harvard Medical School. Whilst a medical student, he demonstrated his intelligence and ability for research (2), and secured two years post-graduate surgical training at Massachusetts' General Hospital under the guidance of Dr Edward Churchill.

In 1934, Beecher was charged with the task of reorganising and developing anaesthesiology, which was not, at that time, a recognised specialty in its own right. He was a determined and intelligent man and carried out this task with great success. Following a brief spell studying in Denmark in the laboratory of Nobel Laureate August Krogh, he returned to Boston where he was appointed anaesthetist-in-chief at Massachusetts' General Hospital in 1936 and, in 1941, the Henry Isaiah Dorr Professor of Anaesthesia Research at Harvard University. (3)

Over the next thirty years, Beecher would become a leading expert in his field of anaesthesiology, publishing over 200 scientific papers. He made major scientific contributions, most notably to our understanding of the psychophysiology of pain. (2)

By the 1960s, Beecher had established himself as a widely respected figure in the world of academic medicine. It was with some surprise, therefore, that he published his article, *Ethics and Clinical Research* in June 1966, risking the contempt of his colleagues. His paper, which emphatically revealed the ethical shortcomings of 22 published clinical trials, highlighted to a professional and public audience the scale of unethical practice that was conducted by US physicians on human subjects.

BEECHER AND MEDICAL ETHICS

During the 1950s, Beecher had become increasingly interested in the ethics of human experimentation producing his first major ethics publication in 1959. (3,4) His paper, entitled *Experimentation in Man*, was published in the *Journal of the American Medical Association* (*JAMA*), but did not receive the attention Beecher had hoped. He appreciated that physicians faced a "bewildering" task in deciding between new therapies in pursuit of their patients' best interests, and stated elsewhere in 1959 that "the properly controlled quantitative approach holds the only real hope for dealing with the oncoming flood of new drugs." (5) Beecher felt strongly that inadequate adherence to good ethical practice could undermine this crucial process and consequently stunt the progress of medical science. (6)

Unfortunately, neither his professional colleagues, nor the public press shared his concern, and it was not until the spring of 1965 that a wider audience would acknowledge his concerns. At a conference, convened by the Upjohn Pharmaceutical Company, Beecher discussed what he felt were widespread ethical failings in research involving human beings before a group of journalists in Michigan. His talk, in which he cited the ethical failings of specific research protocols, if not the names of the investigators and institutions, caught the attention of the national press, and the *New York Times* and *Wall Street Journal* reported his conclusions at length. (6) The press interest was no doubt also spiked by the press conference called by two of Beecher's Harvard colleagues to refute his claims. Whatever the reason, Beecher, at last had his audience.

He submitted a modified version of his presentation for publication in *JAMA* in 1965. (7) It contained over 30 instances where the rights of a patient or research subject had, in Beecher's opinion, been violated in some manner, and once again he concealed the identity of the researchers. This was rejected for publication by the editor following its review. However, this failed to temper Beecher's determination and in the following year, a revised version of the article, containing a description of 22 unethical research protocols, was accepted for publication by the *New England Journal of Medicine* (*NEJM*). (8)

All of the examples illustrated by Beecher placed the subjects' health and well being at risk without their consent. In all but two of the examples from Beecher's original collection of fifty cases there is no mention of consent. (6) Furthermore, these trials were not conducted by rogue investigators from peripheral institutions. They were all published in prominent, well-respected medical journals and conducted in the mainstream, and Beecher noted:

> *I am aware that these are troubling charges. They have grown out of troubling practices. They can be documented, as I propose to do, by examples from leading medical schools, university hospitals, private hospitals, governmental military departments (the Army, the Navy and the Air Force), governmental institutes (the National Institutes of Health), Veterans Administration hospitals and industry. The basis for the charges is broad.* (8)

Beecher concluded his discussion by highlighting his most basic belief about the ethics of clinical research:

> *An experiment is ethical or not at its inception; it does not become ethical* post hoc *— ends do not justify means. There is no ethical distinction between ends and means.* (8)

RESPONSE TO *ETHICS AND CLINICAL RESEARCH*

Ethics in Clinical Research received widespread attention in the national press, but the response from the medical community was initially subdued. Beecher wrote to the editor of the *NEJM* two weeks after the publication of his article stating that he had not received "a single angry letter, but many from this medical community with warm support."(9) First hand reports from Beecher's colleagues at Massachusetts' General Hospital tell of a mixed response. Some of his colleagues who were involved in clinical research felt that this was an attack on their own methods, whilst others treated the revelations with indifference. Many of the younger investigators, however, were convinced that Beecher was correct. His contributions were acknowledged within his own institution when he was appointed chairman of the recently established Harvard Commission on Human Rights. (10)

Henry Knowles Beecher had led a distinguished career in academic medicine. His 1966 article highlighted to a national audience the difficulties encountered in clinical research and inspired greater awareness and discussion amongst medical investigators as to their responsibility to protect the rights of their subjects. He received plaudits for his courage and is respected today as one of the most influential figures in the development of the ethical review process.

Inseparable, however, from a discussion of Beecher and his exposure of unethical research practices is the parallel story of his English contemporary, Maurice Henry Pappworth (fig.2).

MAURICE H. PAPPWORTH

Maurice H. Pappworth was born in Liverpool on 9 January, 1910. He was a gifted student and studied medicine at the University of Liverpool. In 1936, he gained membership to the Royal College of Physicians and hoped to make a successful career in hospital consultancy in London. However, despite a "distinguished career as a junior physician" (2) and a whole-hearted contribution to the war [he became a lieutenant-colonel in charge of a hospital in Bombay (11)], he failed to achieve his

Figure 2. Maurice H. Pappworth (1910-94). (Photograph courtesy of Ngaire and Hilary Watson.)

goal. Pappworth certainly did not fit the mould of a typical London hospital consultant and was, apparently, the subject of anti-semitism; being told following an interview for a consultant post, "no Jew could ever be a gentleman." (12)

Pappworth abandoned his ambition of hospital consultancy and instead opted to become a private medical tutor, coaching students for their examinations for Membership of the Royal College of Physicians (MRCP). As gifted a teacher, as he was a student, Pappworth angered those at the Royal College, who felt he was interfering with their business. At a time when the pass rate for MRCP examinations was less than 15%, Pappworth's students had much greater success. Understandably irked, one examiner once asked him "what exactly do you teach these fellows?" Pappworth replied, perhaps with a mind to his view of the College's exam format, "I just teach them tricks." (12)

PAPPWORTH AND MEDICAL ETHICS

Like Beecher, Pappworth began to become concerned with medical ethics during the 1950s. He was greatly troubled by tales of unethical clinical research, recounted to him by his students, which took place, seemingly at large, in British hospitals. The promotion of a junior doctor in large teaching hospitals depended heavily not on his or her clinical ability, but on their published works and this, Pappworth felt, contributed to poor research practices and the compromise of patient safety. (13) He began to write in protest to those journals that published studies, which were, in his opinion, unethical, but these were often rejected. (13)

In 1962, he was approached by *Twentieth Century* magazine to contribute to a series entitled *Doctors in the Sixties*. Pappworth submitted an article, in language aimed at the general public, describing fourteen medical experiments, which he felt were unethical. His article, entitled *Human Guinea Pigs: A Warning,* caused an immediate stir. It was reported widely in the national press and was the subject of several television features. The debate regarding ethical experimentation on human subjects had come to life and Pappworth was the subject of both congratulations and condemnation from lay and medical communities. In the same year, Pappworth completed his book, *Human Guinea Pigs: Experimentation in Man,* which contained over 200 unethical clinical investigations carried out in the UK and the US. However, due to legal reasons, it would not appear in print until 1967. (14) In the opening pages, he set out his justification for writing the book:

> *Most of those doctors who know that these things are common practice have felt powerless to stop them; while the public, for its part, has remained unaware of what is going on.* (14)

In the book he explains not only the circumstances under which the ethics of an experiment are compromised, but, in contrast to Beecher, cites fully the names of the investigators who undertook the research and the institutions in which it took place. The examples described included experiments conducted on children, incapacitated adults, pregnant women, the elderly and the dying. When assessing the unethical practices he had uncovered, he likened them to those conducted during the Second World War. Nazi doctors, he argued, were: "…not *in principle* different from an experimenting doctor, in a hospital here or in America…" And, conceded that: "This is a terrible thing to have to say…" (14)

RESPONSE TO *HUMAN GUINEA PIGS*

Unlike Beecher, the eminent Harvard Professor, Pappworth was very much a peripheral figure in the medical community and, although his book proved a commercial success (15), he was scorned by the medical profession. Before the book had even been published Pappworth describes how he received anonymous phone calls from senior physicians urging him to withdraw his plans to publish "for the good of the profession." (13) Initially, its publication was largely ignored by the medical press, however a review in the *BMJ* commented positively that, "it would be a good thing for every clinical scientist to read this book."(16) There were further editorials in both the *Lancet* (17) and *BMJ* (18) that agreed in principle with the issues raised in the book whilst demonstrating a seemingly intense resentment towards its author describing his "bitter analysis" as the work of a "dissatisfied man." (17)

While Beecher was praised for his contributions, Pappworth was personally attacked. By revealing the names of the researchers and the institutions at which the described experiments took place, Pappworth left himself open to abuse from a medical profession wounded by his allegations, but noted that, "giving names and references has, at least in small measure, acted as a deterrent." (12) Certainly the fact that Pappworth was a solitary figure, isolated from the rest of the profession, left him vulnerable to criticism. His determination to highlight the unethical conduct of his contemporaries, meant he was shunned by the medical community. Unaffected, however, he shrugged off criticism from those who tried to silence him:

> *My opinion remains that those who dirty the linen and not those who wash it should be criticised. Some do not wash dirty linen in public or in private and the dirt is merely left to accumulate until it stinks.* (13)

In 1993, 57 years after passing his MRCP, Maurice Pappworth was finally welcomed back inside the medical fold and awarded his Fellowship of the Royal College of Physicians, accompanied by a standing ovation. (19, 20) His death, the following year, was marked by a single obituary in the British press – that this appeared in the appropriately named *Independent* newspaper is perhaps a fitting memorial. (20)

Both Beecher and Pappworth were complex characters, who shared a number of common traits including a strong sense of morality, great tenacity in the face of rejection and the courage to face the censure of their peers. Equally there were also marked differences: Beecher was at the very centre of his profession, Pappworth on its periphery; Beecher a highly respected Harvard academic, Pappworth an anomaly in his profession, working as a private post-graduate medical tutor. What motivated each in their whistle-blowing? In order to answer this question we must first look at the phenomenon of whistle-blowing in more detail.

WHISTLE-BLOWING

When does feedback become formal peer-review; when does it become criticism; and when does it become whistle-blowing? Clearly, when it comes to raising concerns, there is a spectrum of critique, just as there is a range of motivations that underpin these actions.

Whistle-blowing has been described simply as, "making a disclosure in the public interest"(21), but more fully in the context of medicine as, "the attempt, in good faith and in the public interest, to disclose and resolve in a reasonable and non-vexatious manner, but in the face of significant institutional or professional opposition, a significant deficiency in the quality or safety of health care." (22) Acknowledged in the latter definition is the existence of a range of whistle-blowing-like activities that derive, not from any virtuous motivation, but from a desire for vengeance, professional jealously, enmity or simply mischief-making. Indeed, enmity as a motive for apparent whistle-blowing, and its consequences has been described by one victim of such an attack as "intent to damage." (23)

In the past, whistle-blowers have brought down presidents, have called multi-national industries to account, and have destroyed their own careers and even lives.

Mark Felt, the former second in command of the FBI in the early 1970s, revealed himself more than 30 years later as the celebrated "Deep Throat" who had assisted the investigative journalists, Bob Woodward and Carl Bernstein, in uncovering the Watergate Scandal, which led to the downfall of President Nixon in 1974. (24)

Jeffrey Wigand, a tobacco company executive, revealed on television in 1996 how his former employer, Brown & Williamson, had intentionally engineered its tobacco blends to increase the available nicotine in cigarette smoke. (25) His allegations led to major law-suits and the regulation of tobacco advertising.

Ignaz Semmelweis, an Austro-Hungarian obstetrician, while working at the Vienna General Hospital in 1847, realized that poor hygiene amongst the doctors was responsible for the transmission of puerperal fever to women in the obstetric wards. Although he successfully proved his hypothesis his findings were met with scorn from his peers and his contract was not renewed. His career went into decline and after developing mental illness he was institutionalized where the staff beat him to death (22).

These are just three examples of whistle-blowers from many. Throughout history they have been:

> *ostracised, pressured to drop allegations, and threatened with counterallegations. They lose desirable assignments, have their research support reduced and their promotions and raises denied. Their contracts are not renewed, and they are fired.* (26)

In such a judgemental and punitive environment, where those who raise concerns about their professional colleagues are subjected to greater censure than those who have caused the concern in the first place, what could possibly motivate one to go public?

Desires for fame and fortune, although often cited, are unlikely to be prime factors, especially since dismissal and notoriety are commoner outcomes. (12) Rather, frustration with the lack of concern shown by their institutions or professional bodies, coupled with an overwhelming need to see a wrong exposed and patients protected, have compelled many whistle-blowers to publish their concerns. This may be in the form of journal papers or books, as in the case of Beecher and Pappworth, or in more recent years may involve going directly to the press, television or internet.

Going public in this way, however, is a one-way path. Indeed, whistle-blowers have been likened to bees: they have just one sting to use, and using it may result in career suicide. (27) Nevertheless, although the costs may be high in both professional and personal terms, many conscientious professionals are not willing to turn a blind eye to unethical behaviour or professional misconduct. Indeed it has been noted that whistle-blowers are "motivated chiefly by conscience and professional virtue" (22) and are willing to risk the inevitable consequences of their actions.

In our opening chapter we discussed the notion of virtue theory as being one of the moral frameworks within which we may live and work. This theory is built upon the concept of the virtuous character of the individual rather than any concern with the innate goodness of an action or the good of its consequences. Whistle-blowing may be seen as a prime exemplar of the virtues of benevolence, righteousness and courage. While we may all strive to possess such virtues, it is clear that few us are able to put them into practice, as whistle-blowing remains a response of the minority, especially within medicine.

Within academic medicine the problems for the potential whistle-blower have been expertly reviewed by Rhodes and Strain who note that the design of academic institutions: "(1) systematically ignores serious ethical problems, (2) regards whistleblowers as enemies of the institution and punishes them, and (3) thereby fails to provide an ethical environment." (26) These authors propose a transformation of academic medicine where whistle-blowers should no longer be viewed as the "enemy within" but as institutional friends. Drawing a comparison with the regulation of animal experimentation where any violation of the code of practice puts the work of all investigators in an institution in jeopardy, they propose that such a "forceful policing from powerful extra-institutional review" may be the best solution to create a supportive, morally aware environment for academic medicine.

Interestingly, such a system already exists in the UK when we consider the conduct of clinical trials of investigational medicinal products. The Medicines and Healthcare Products Regulatory Agency (MHRA) has the legal mandate to inspect any institution sponsoring such a clinical trial and has the authority to suspend its operations if it finds sufficient cause. Such a suspension will adversely affect any investigator working within that institution. There is therefore a strong incentive amongst investigators to be aware of any wrongdoing and to report it promptly – if for no other reason than to ensure the continuity of their own work. Whistle-blowing thus becomes a valued institutional responsibility that should be welcomed.

Self-protection, however, is not the primary motive for most whistle-blowers, and nor should it be. Rather it should be ingrained into our very professionalism. In the UK, the British Medical Association states very clearly in its guidance for NHS doctors that we all have responsibility to report on unethical practices in clinical research, noting: "Whilst ethical approval can be taken as a guide, if you see problems that perhaps the ethics committee did not see then it is still your duty to say or do something about it." (28)

The protection of whistle-blowers has, in recent years, become a major concern for governments. In the UK, as in the US, there are specific laws designed to protect anyone raising concerns. The UK's Public Interest Disclosure Act 1998 provides a legal framework for the protection of whistle-blowers with regards to victimization or dismissal from their jobs. The scope of the Act extends to the raising of "genuine concerns about crime, civil offences…, miscarriage of justice, danger to health and safety or the environment and the cover up of any of these." (29)

In any human endeavour, mistakes will be made. The fact that they occur should not necessarily be a cause for approbation; that they occur and are covered up and ignored, should be. Physicians and scientists should work in a professionally liberated environment, because as Gandhi has written: "Freedom is not worth having if it does not connote freedom to err and even to sin."(30) However, our freedom to make a mistake does not preclude it from also being a sobering, educational experience. By acknowledging our own errors and those of others, by discussing them openly, and by learning from them we can push back the limits of our ignorance and shed ever-increasing light on our practice. This is as true for the field of clinical research as any other.

CONCLUSIONS

It is claimed that all that is necessary for the triumph of evil is for good men to do nothing. Henry K. Beecher and Maurice H. Pappworth were good men and brave physicians, who held up the practices of their peers to the glare of professional and public scrutiny. Their contributions were made at significant personal expense and marked a watershed in the development of research ethics. What lesson can we learn from their stories? Simply, that time and again, patients are protected by the actions of good men, and women. Far from being an academic exercise, ethics in action can be an ugly affair, for sometimes it pits colleague against colleague. Feelings can be hurt, careers destroyed, lives damaged: but ultimately the welfare of our patients is what matters, and it is this that drives those who feel compelled to raise the alarm, and blow the whistle.

REFERENCES

1. Greene NM. Obituary: Henry Knowles Beecher 1904-1976. *Anesthesiology* 1976; 45: 377-8.
2. Edelson PJ. Henry K Beecher and Maurice Pappworth: informed consent in human experimentation and the physicians' response. In: *Informed consent and medical research*. Doyal L and Tobias JS (Eds). BMJ Books, London 2001.
3. Best M, Neuhauser D. Henry K Beecher: pain, belief and truth at the bedside. The powerful placebo, ethical research and anaesthesia safety. *Quality and Safety in Health Care* 2010; 19: 466-8.
4. Beecher HK. Experimentation in man. *Journal of the American Medical Association* 1959; 169: 461-78.
5. Beecher HK. *Measurement of Subjective Responses*. Oxford University Press, Oxford 1959.
6. Rothman DJ. *Strangers at the Bedside: A history of how law and bioethics transformed medical decision making*. Aldine Transaction, Piscataway, 2003.
7. Harkness J, Lederer SE, Wikler D. Laying ethical foundations for clinical research. *Bulletin of the World Health Organization* 2001, 79: 365-6.
8. Beecher HK. Ethics and clinical research. *New England Journal of Medicine*. 1966; 274: 1354-60.
9. Kopp VJ. Henry Knowles Beecher and the development of informed consent in anesthesia research. *Anesthesiology* 1999; 90: 1756-65.
10. Bunker JP. Commentary on "Ethics and clinical research". In: *Informed consent and medical research*. Doyal L and Tobias JS (Eds). BMJ Books, London, 2001.
11. Lock S. Commentary on Human Guinea Pigs. In: *Informed consent and medical research*. Doyal L and Tobias JS (Eds). BMJ Books, London, 2001.
12. Booth C. Obituary: M H Pappworth MD, FRCP. *British Medical Journal* 1994; 309; 1577.

13. Pappworth MH. "Human guinea pigs"-a history. *British Medical Journal* 1990; 301: 1456-60.

14. Pappworth MH. *Human guinea pigs: experimentation on man.* Routledge and Kegan Paul, London, 1967.

15. Eastwood M. Medical Classics: Human Guinea Pigs. *British Medical Journal* 2009; 339: b5113.

16. Witts LJ. Experiments on Man. *British Medical Journal* 1967; 2: 689.

17. Editorial. Responsibilities of research. *Lancet* 1967; 1: 1020.

18. Editorial. Experimental Medicine. *British Medical Journal* 1967; 2: 1108.

19. Watson MH. Maurice Henry Pappworth MRCP (1936) FRCP (1993). *Fellowship Affairs* 1997, April, 29-31.

20. Lock S. Obituary: Dr Maurice Pappworth. *The Independent* 12 November 1994.

21. Chartered Institute of Personnel & Development http://www.cipd.co.uk/subjects/empreltns/whistleblw/ whistle.htm [Accessed: 02 December, 2010].

22. Bolsin S, Faunce T, Oakley J. Practical virtue ethics: healthcare whistleblowing and portable digital technology. *Journal of Medical Ethics* 2005; 31: 612-8.

23. Anon. Whistleblowing or professional assassination. *British Medical Journal* 1998; 316: 1756-7.

24. O'Connor JD. "I'm the guy they called Deep Throat" *Vanity Fair* July 2005.

25. CBS *60 Minutes* February 4, 1996 Transcript available at http://www.jeffreywigand.com/60minutes.php [Accessed: 02 December, 2010]

26. Rhodes R, Strain JJ. Whistleblowing in academic medicine. *Journal of Medical Ethics* 2004; 30: 35-9.

27. Vinten G. Whistle while you work in the health-related professions? *Journal of the Royal Society of Health* 1994; 114: 256–62.

28. BMA. Whistleblowing. *Advice for BMA members working in NHS secondary care about raising concerns in the workplace June*

2009. Available at http://www.bma.org.uk/images/ Whistleblowing_tcm41-156406.pdf [Accessed: 01 December, 2010]

29. Public Interest Disclosure Act 1998. Available at http://www.legislation.gov.uk/ukpga/1998/23/contents [Accessed: 01 December, 2010].

30. Gandhi MK. *Young India* 1931; XIII: 31.

··■··

APPENDIX I

THE NUREMBERG CODE

from *Trials of War Criminals before the Nuremberg Military Tribunals under Control Council Law No. 10.* Nuremberg, October 1946– April 1949. Washington, DC: U.S. G.P.O, 1949–1953.

Permissible Medical Experiments

The great weight of the evidence before us is to the effect that certain types of medical experiments on human beings, when kept within reasonably well-defined bounds, conform to the ethics of the medical profession generally. The protagonists of the practice of human experimentation justify their views on the basis that such experiments yield results for the good of society that are unprocurable by other methods or means of study. All agree, however, that certain basic principles must be observed in order to satisfy moral, ethical and legal concepts:

1. The voluntary consent of the human subject is absolutely essential.

   This means that the person involved should have legal capacity to give consent; should be so situated as to be able to exercise free power of choice, without the intervention of any element of force, fraud, deceit, duress, over-reaching, or other ulterior form of constraint or coercion; and should have sufficient knowledge and comprehension of the elements of the subject matter involved as to enable him to make an understanding and enlightened decision. This latter element requires that before the acceptance of an affirmative decision by the experimental subject there should be made known to him the nature, duration, and purpose of the experiment; the method and means by which it is to be conducted; all inconveniences and hazards reasonably to be expected; and the effects upon his health or person which may possibly come from his participation in the experiment.

   The duty and responsibility for ascertaining the quality of the consent rests upon each individual who initiates, directs or engages in the experiment. It is a personal duty and responsibility which may not be delegated to another with impunity.

2. The experiment should be such as to yield fruitful results for the good of society, unprocurable by other methods or means of study, and not random and unnecessary in nature.

3. The experiment should be so designed and based on the results of animal experimentation and a knowledge of the natural history of the disease or other problem under study that the anticipated results will justify the performance of the experiment.

4. The experiment should be so conducted as to avoid all unnecessary physical and mental suffering and injury.

5. No experiment should be conducted where there is an a priori reason to believe that death or disabling injury will occur; except, perhaps, in those experiments where the experimental physicians also serve as subjects.

6. The degree of risk to be taken should never exceed that determined by the humanitarian importance of the problem to be solved by the experiment.

7. Proper preparations should be made and adequate facilities provided to protect the experimental subject against even remote possibilities of injury, disability, or death.

8. The experiment should be conducted only by scientifically qualified persons. The highest degree of skill and care should be required through all stages of the experiment of those who conduct or engage in the experiment.

9. During the course of the experiment the human subject should be at liberty to bring the experiment to an end if he has reached the physical or mental state where continuation of the experiment seems to him to be impossible.

10. During the course of the experiment the scientist in charge must be prepared to terminate the experiment at any stage, if he has probably cause to believe, in the exercise of the good faith, superior skill and careful judgment required of him that a continuation of the experiment is likely to result in injury, disability, or death to the experimental subject.

APPENDIX 2

THE DECLARATION OF HELSINKI

(Reproduced with permission of the World Medical Association.)

WORLD MEDICAL ASSOCIATION DECLARATION OF HELSINKI
Ethical Principles for Medical Research Involving Human Subjects

Adopted by the 18th WMA General Assembly, Helsinki, Finland, June 1964, and amended by the:

29th WMA General Assembly, Tokyo, Japan, October 1975

35th WMA General Assembly, Venice, Italy, October 1983

41st WMA General Assembly, Hong Kong, September 1989

48th WMA General Assembly, Somerset West, Republic of South Africa, October 1996

52nd WMA General Assembly, Edinburgh, Scotland, October 2000

53rd WMA General Assembly, Washington 2002 (Note of Clarification on paragraph 29 added)

55th WMA General Assembly, Tokyo 2004 (Note of Clarification on Paragraph 30 added)

59th WMA General Assembly, Seoul, October 2008

A. INTRODUCTION

1. The World Medical Association (WMA) has developed the Declaration of Helsinki as a statement of ethical principles for medical research involving human subjects, including research on identifiable human material and data.

The Declaration is intended to be read as a whole and each of its constituent paragraphs should not be applied without consideration of all other relevant paragraphs.

2. Although the Declaration is addressed primarily to physicians, the WMA encourages other participants in medical research involving human subjects to adopt these principles.

3. It is the duty of the physician to promote and safeguard the health of patients, including those who are involved in medical research. The physician's knowledge and conscience are dedicated to the fulfilment of this duty.

4. The Declaration of Geneva of the WMA binds the physician with the words, "The health of my patient will be my first consideration," and the International Code of Medical Ethics declares that, "A physician shall act in the patient's best interest when providing medical care."

5. Medical progress is based on research that ultimately must include studies involving human subjects. Populations that are underrepresented in medical research should be provided appropriate access to participation in research.

6. In medical research involving human subjects, the well-being of the individual research subject must take precedence over all other interests.

7. The primary purpose of medical research involving human subjects is to understand the causes, development and effects of diseases and improve preventive, diagnostic and therapeutic interventions (methods, procedures and treatments). Even the best current interventions must be evaluated continually through research for their safety, effectiveness, efficiency, accessibility and quality.

8. In medical practice and in medical research, most interventions involve risks and burdens.

9. Medical research is subject to ethical standards that promote respect for all human subjects and protect their health and rights. Some research populations are particularly vulnerable and need special protection. These include those who cannot give or refuse consent for themselves and those who may be vulnerable to coercion or undue influence.

10. Physicians should consider the ethical, legal and regulatory norms and standards for research involving human subjects in their own countries as well as applicable international norms and standards. No national or international ethical, legal or regulatory requirement should reduce or eliminate any of the protections for research subjects set forth in this Declaration.

B. PRINCIPLES FOR ALL MEDICAL RESEARCH

11. It is the duty of physicians who participate in medical research to protect the life, health, dignity, integrity, right to self-determination, privacy, and confidentiality of personal information of research subjects.

12. Medical research involving human subjects must conform to generally accepted scientific principles, be based on a thorough knowledge of the scientific literature, other relevant sources of information, and adequate laboratory and, as appropriate, animal experimentation. The welfare of animals used for research must be respected.

13. Appropriate caution must be exercised in the conduct of medical research that may harm the environment.

14. The design and performance of each research study involving human subjects must be clearly described in a research protocol. The protocol should contain a statement of the ethical considerations involved and should indicate how the principles in this Declaration have been addressed. The protocol should include information regarding funding, sponsors, institutional affiliations, other potential conflicts of interest, incentives for subjects and provisions for treating and/or compensating subjects who are harmed as a consequence of participation in the research study. The protocol should describe arrangements for post-study access by study subjects to interventions identified as beneficial in the study or access to other appropriate care or benefits.

15. The research protocol must be submitted for consideration, comment, guidance and approval to a research ethics committee before

the study begins. This committee must be independent of the researcher, the sponsor and any other undue influence. It must take into consideration the laws and regulations of the country or countries in which the research is to be performed as well as applicable international norms and standards but these must not be allowed to reduce or eliminate any of the protections for research subjects set forth in this Declaration. The committee must have the right to monitor ongoing studies. The researcher must provide monitoring information to the committee, especially information about any serious adverse events. No change to the protocol may be made without consideration and approval by the committee.

16. Medical research involving human subjects must be conducted only by individuals with the appropriate scientific training and qualifications. Research on patients or healthy volunteers requires the supervision of a competent and appropriately qualified physician or other health care professional. The responsibility for the protection of research subjects must always rest with the physician or other health care professional and never the research subjects, even though they have given consent.

17. Medical research involving a disadvantaged or vulnerable population or community is only justified if the research is responsive to the health needs and priorities of this population or community and if there is a reasonable likelihood that this population or community stands to benefit from the results of the research.

18. Every medical research study involving human subjects must be preceded by careful assessment of predictable risks and burdens to the individuals and communities involved in the research in comparison with foreseeable benefits to them and to other individuals or communities affected by the condition under investigation.

19. Every clinical trial must be registered in a publicly accessible database before recruitment of the first subject.

20. Physicians may not participate in a research study involving human subjects unless they are confident that the risks involved have been adequately assessed and can be satisfactorily managed. Physicians must immediately stop a study when the risks are found to outweigh the

potential benefits or when there is conclusive proof of positive and beneficial results.

21. Medical research involving human subjects may only be conducted if the importance of the objective outweighs the inherent risks and burdens to the research subjects.

22. Participation by competent individuals as subjects in medical research must be voluntary. Although it may be appropriate to consult family members or community leaders, no competent individual may be enrolled in a research study unless he or she freely agrees.

23. Every precaution must be taken to protect the privacy of research subjects and the confidentiality of their personal information and to minimize the impact of the study on their physical, mental and social integrity.

24. In medical research involving competent human subjects, each potential subject must be adequately informed of the aims, methods, sources of funding, any possible conflicts of interest, institutional affiliations of the researcher, the anticipated benefits and potential risks of the study and the discomfort it may entail, and any other relevant aspects of the study. The potential subject must be informed of the right to refuse to participate in the study or to withdraw consent to participate at any time without reprisal. Special attention should be given to the specific information needs of individual potential subjects as well as to the methods used to deliver the information. After ensuring that the potential subject has understood the information, the physician or another appropriately qualified individual must then seek the potential subject's freely-given informed consent, preferably in writing. If the consent cannot be expressed in writing, the non-written consent must be formally documented and witnessed.

25. For medical research using identifiable human material or data, physicians must normally seek consent for the collection, analysis, storage and/or reuse. There may be situations where consent would be impossible or impractical to obtain for such research or would pose a threat to the validity of the research. In such situations the research

may be done only after consideration and approval of a research ethics committee.

26. When seeking informed consent for participation in a research study the physician should be particularly cautious if the potential subject is in a dependent relationship with the physician or may consent under duress. In such situations the informed consent should be sought by an appropriately qualified individual who is completely independent of this relationship.

27. For a potential research subject who is incompetent, the physician must seek informed consent from the legally authorized representative. These individuals must not be included in a research study that has no likelihood of benefit for them unless it is intended to promote the health of the population represented by the potential subject, the research cannot instead be performed with competent persons, and the research entails only minimal risk and minimal burden.

28. When a potential research subject who is deemed incompetent is able to give assent to decisions about participation in research, the physician must seek that assent in addition to the consent of the legally authorized representative. The potential subject's dissent should be respected.

29. Research involving subjects who are physically or mentally incapable of giving consent, for example, unconscious patients, may be done only if the physical or mental condition that prevents giving informed consent is a necessary characteristic of the research population. In such circumstances the physician should seek informed consent from the legally authorized representative. If no such representative is available and if the research cannot be delayed, the study may proceed without informed consent provided that the specific reasons for involving subjects with a condition that renders them unable to give informed consent have been stated in the research protocol and the study has been approved by a research ethics committee. Consent to remain in the research should be obtained as soon as possible from the subject or a legally authorized representative.

30. Authors, editors and publishers all have ethical obligations with regard to the publication of the results of research. Authors have a duty to make publicly available the results of their research on human subjects and are accountable for the completeness and accuracy of their reports. They should adhere to accepted guidelines for ethical reporting. Negative and inconclusive as well as positive results should be published or otherwise made publicly available. Sources of funding, institutional affiliations and conflicts of interest should be declared in the publication. Reports of research not in accordance with the principles of this Declaration should not be accepted for publication.

C. ADDITIONAL PRINCIPLES FOR MEDICAL RESEARCH COMBINED WITH MEDICAL CARE

31. The physician may combine medical research with medical care only to the extent that the research is justified by its potential preventive, diagnostic or therapeutic value and if the physician has good reason to believe that participation in the research study will not adversely affect the health of the patients who serve as research subjects.

32. The benefits, risks, burdens and effectiveness of a new intervention must be tested against those of the best current proven intervention, except in the following circumstances:

• The use of placebo, or no treatment, is acceptable in studies where no current proven intervention exists; or
• Where for compelling and scientifically sound methodological reasons the use of placebo is necessary to determine the efficacy or safety of an intervention and the patients who receive placebo or no treatment will not be subject to any risk of serious or irreversible harm. Extreme care must be taken to avoid abuse of this option.

33. At the conclusion of the study, patients entered into the study are entitled to be informed about the outcome of the study and to share any benefits that result from it, for example, access to interventions identified as beneficial in the study or to other appropriate care or benefits.

34. The physician must fully inform the patient which aspects of the care are related to the research. The refusal of a patient to participate in a study or the patient's decision to withdraw from the study must never interfere with the patient-physician relationship.

35. In the treatment of a patient, where proven interventions do not exist or have been ineffective, the physician, after seeking expert advice, with informed consent from the patient or a legally authorized representative, may use an unproven intervention if in the physician's judgement it offers hope of saving life, re-establishing health or alleviating suffering. Where possible, this intervention should be made the object of research, designed to evaluate its safety and efficacy. In all cases, new information should be recorded and, where appropriate, made publicly available.

·■■·

APPENDIX 3

PRINCIPLES AND CONDITIONS OF GOOD CLINICAL PRACTICE (GCP)

The 14 Principles and conditions outlined below are from UK Statutory Instrument 2006/1928 Schedule 1, Part 2. They are governed by UK law for all clinical trials of investigational medicinal products (CTIMP). The 13 Core Principles of ICH GCP (see the E6 Document) should be applied to all non-CTIMP trials.

GCP Principles & Conditions

1. The rights, safety and well-being of the trial subjects shall prevail over the interests of science and society.

2. Each individual involved in conducting a trial shall be qualified by education, training and experience to perform his tasks.

3. Clinical trials shall be scientifically sound and guided by ethical principles in all their aspects.

4. The necessary procedures to secure the quality of every aspect of the trial shall be complied with.

5. The available non-clinical information on an investigational medicinal product shall be adequate to support the proposed clinical trial.

6. Clinical trials shall be conducted in accordance with the principles of the Declaration of Helsinki.

7. The protocol shall provide for the definition of inclusion and exclusion of subjects participating in a clinical trial, monitoring and publication policy.

8. The investigator and sponsor shall consider all relevant guidance with respect to commencing and conducting a clinical trial.

9. All clinical information shall be recorded, handled and stored in such a way that it can be accurately reported, interpreted and verified, while the confidentiality of records of the trial subject remains protected.

10. Before the trial is initiated, foreseeable risks and inconveniences have been weighed against the anticipated benefit for the individual trial subject and other present and future patients. A trial should be initiated and continued only if the anticipated benefits justify the risks.

11. The medical care given to, and medical decisions made on behalf of, subjects shall always be the responsibility of an appropriately qualified doctor or, when appropriate, of a qualified dentist.

12. A trial shall be initiated only if an ethics committee and the licensing authority comes to the conclusion that the anticipated therapeutic and public health benefits justify the risks and may be continued only if compliance with this requirement is permanently monitored.

13. The rights of each subject to physical and mental integrity, to privacy and to the protection of the data concerning him in accordance with the Data Protection Act 1998 are safeguarded.

14. Provision has been made for insurance or indemnity to cover the liability of the investigator and sponsor which may arise in relation to the clinical trial.

· ∎ · ·

SUGGESTIONS FOR FURTHER READING

Hopefully, after you have read this book, you may be stimulated to read more on the topics discussed here. There is, however, a bewildering array of books written on many of the topics discussed in this book. So where should you begin? Below, we list some that we have found particularly helpful and which you may find interesting. Should you wish to obtain any of these suggested texts you will find them by searching on Amazon. Alternatively, you will find them all listed separately at the Amazon Bookstore on the website www.allangaw.com

Chapter 1 – A moral framework

Kant I. (1785/1948) (Paton HJ – translation and commentary) *The Moral Law: Groundwork of the Metaphysics of Morals*. Routledge Classics, London.

> If you are coming to Kant for the first time this is one of his shortest and most important works. This edition, translated by HJ Paton, also has an extensive commentary that is both well written and makes Kant's, sometimes impenetrable, arguments accessible.

Ross WD. (1930/2002). *The Right and the Good*. Reprinted with an introduction by Philip Stratton-Lake. Oxford University Press, Oxford.

> The original work of David Ross reprinted with a very useful introduction by a contemporary philosopher.

LaFollette H. (Ed) (2007) *Ethics in Practice. An Anthology*, 3rd Edition, Blackwell Publishing, Oxford.

At almost 750 pages this is a weighty tome, but one that is packed with 67 excellent articles on a wide range of practical ethical issues. The first section provides an ideal introduction to Ethical Theory.

Shafer-Landau R. (Ed) (2007) *Ethical Theory. An Anthology*. Blackwell Publishing, Oxford.

If you want more on Ethical Theory and would like an accessible anthology of original works this book is ideal.

Chapter 2 – Research into practice

Bown, S. (2003) *Scurvy: How a Surgeon, a Mariner and a Gentleman Solved the Greatest Medical Mystery of the Age of the Sail*. Summersdale, Chichester.

Popular medical history at its best – an excellent and highly readable account of the history of scurvy and the role of James Lind in its conquest.

Harvie DI. (2002) *Limeys: The Conquest of Scurvy*. Sutton Publishing Ltd, Stroud.

An alternative to Bown, and another well presented history of Scurvy, Vitamin C and Lind's contribution.

Chapter 3 – The investigator-participant relationship

Emanuel EJ, Lie RK, Grady C, Miller FG, Crouch RA, Wendler D. (Eds) (2008) *The Oxford Textbook of Clinical Research Ethics*. Oxford University Press, Oxford.

This is the most comprehensive and useful compendium of articles on clinical research ethics available and would be an invaluable resource for any research unit's library.

Chapter 4 – Informed consent

Pierce JR and Writer JV. (2005) *Yellow Jack: How Yellow Fever Ravaged America and Walter Reed Discovered its Deadly Secrets.* John Wiley & Sons Inc, Hoboken.

Part detailed history, part adventure story; this excellent book retraces the story of Yellow Fever from its first appearances 350 years ago to the Cuban research conducted by Reed and his colleagues that ultimately helped control the disease.

Doyal L and Tobias JS (Eds). (2001) *Informed consent and medical research.* BMJ Books, London.

This book has an unparalleled collection of essays on various aspects of informed consent as well as reprints of key documents including Beecher's 1966 paper *Ethics and Clinical Research.*

Chapter 5 – Codes of ethical practice

Annas J and Grodin MA (Eds). (1995) *The Nazi Doctors and the Nuremberg Code: Human Rights in Human Experimentation.* OUP USA.

A multi-author book containing a wealth of useful material and commentary on the development of the Nuremberg Code.

Lifton RJ. (1988) *The Nazi Doctors: Medical Killing and the Psychology of Genocide.* Basic Books, New York.

A large and painstakingly researched book, which goes further than most books of this genre in examining the thought processes of the Nazi medical personnel.

Schmidt U. (2004) *Justice at Nuremberg: Leo Alexander and the Nazi Doctors' Trial.* Palgrave Macmillan, Basingstoke.

As the title suggests this book focuses on the part played by the Austrian/American physician Leo Alexander at the Nuremberg Trial and his part in the development of the Nuremberg Code. A thoroughly researched and well-written work.

Schmidt U. (2007) *Karl Brandt - The Nazi Doctor: Medicine and Power in the Third Reich.* Hambledon Continuum, London.

Schmidt's next book – this time focussing on Hitler's personal physician and the most senior defendant at the Doctors' Trial in Nuremberg.

Weindling PJ. (2006) *Nazi Medicine and the Nuremberg Trials: From Medical War Crimes to Informed Consent.* Palgrave Macmillan, Basingstoke.

A very detailed exposition and analysis of the Doctors' Trial itself.

Chapter 6 – Whistle-blowing

Pappworth MH. (1967) *Human guinea pigs: experimentation on man.* Routledge and Kegan Paul, London.

As troubling and direct today as when it was written more than 40 years ago, Maurice Pappworth's book is essential reading for anyone interested in the development of the research ethics movement in the 1960s.

Nuland SB. (2003) *The Doctors' Plague: Germs, Childbed Fever and the Strange Story of Ignac Semmelweis.* Norton, New York.

This inspiring story of one of medicine's first whistle-blowers presents Semmelweis as a flawed hero. The story is fascinating as medical history and sobering as it recounts the potential consequences of criticising one's professional peers.

·■·

INDEX